THE FEEDING OF RUMINANTS
PRINCIPLES AND PRACTICE

by

E R ØRSKOV

Rowett Research Institute, Aberdeen

CHALCOMBE PUBLICATIONS

First published in Great Britain by
Chalcombe Publications,13 Highwoods Drive,
Marlow Bottom, Marlow, Bucks SL7 3PU.

May 1987

© E.R. Ørskov 1987

ISBN   0948617 09 8

Cover design: S & L Creative Services

Illustrations: Joan Ørskov

Printed in Great Britain

CONTENTS

INTRODUCTION

I have often been encouraged by farmers, students and friends with a practical bent to write a book on feeding of ruminant livestock. This book should incorporate new scientific knowledge of feeding but in a language readily understood by practical people.

It must be understood from the outset that I am not a farm adviser. My qualifications are simply that my research career has been one of unravelling scientific principles of nutrition, but since I come from a dairy farm and farm in some of my spare time I hope I can still communicate in the language of practical people.

I must point out here also that I take issue with those scientists who find difficulties in explaining scientific principles to farmers with the consequence that when they do, science is reduced and communicated in a child's language. To me it is only a question of language. The same science is explained, although perhaps less precisely. I hope I have achieved this.

The feeding of ruminants in general has been surrounded by a great deal of mystery and indeed still is. Cowmen have their own proven recipes which may or may not have a scientific foundation but nevertheless are fervently believed in.

There are two very good reasons why the feeding of ruminants has been more of an art than a science. Firstly, the stomach in the mature ruminant is a large fermentation vat where a multitude of micro-organisms flourish. Like any other fermentation it is important that conditions are stable. It may well be compared to winemaking, with each animal having its own fermentation vat. The stockman is able to influence the fermentation in the stomach in much the same way as the winemaker producing wine. In the society of amateur winemakers there is also a great deal of mystery. Given the same basic ingredients there is little doubt that some winemakers will make a good product while others have less pleasing results. Some stockmen, given the same resources and animals, can achieve good results; others cannot.

The second reason why ruminants are special is that they are very much influenced by their relationship with the environment, including the stockman. This relationship can have a direct influence on their nutrition. For instance, with young animals, lack of understanding of the importance of behaviour can have the effect of leading milk into the fermentation vat or rumen rather than into the true stomach, leading to digestion problems and poor performance. All in all, it is easy to understand that the feeding of ruminant livestock has been a source of lively debate among stockmen for many hundreds of years, and seldom has it been possible to obtain a concensus of opinion. This intuitive rather than scientific approach to feeding has had disadvantages as it has often left the farmer open to exploitation by shrewd merchants selling products, the benefits of which are, to say the least, questionable. Such products are indeed still being marketed.

Much of the art of feeding of ruminant livestock can now readily be explained. Observant farmers who were able to make systematic observations formulated rules which have now been scientifically documented. For instance some farmers have long believed in feeding fish meal to ewes before lambing as it would make the lambs more viable at birth. There is now scientific support for this. It is more difficult to explain other theories, such as that the feeding of turnips to ewes affects the length of the horns of the lambs at birth!

It is intended in this book to discuss the feeding of ruminant livestock with emphasis on those aspects of ruminant feeding which are now scientifically proven. Whilst there is still a great deal of art in stockmanship, an understanding of how the animal functions can help to ensure that fewer mistakes are made. More important, it can enable the farmer to be more discerning when buying commercial products. An increased understanding of how the animal functions can also have the effect of increasing respect for the animals and the fascination of working with them. Increased knowledge can then increase the pleasure of working for those people whose livelihoods depend on the keeping of ruminant livestock.

CHAPTER 1

THE NEW BORN RUMINANT

The nutrition of the young really begins as soon as the fertilized egg is attached to the wall of the uterus. However, nutrition during pregnancy will be discussed in a later chapter. The new-born ruminant is already at a quite advanced stage of its development. Here it must be remembered that domestic ruminants were selected from wild species, and predators ensured that selection towards fast movement of the newborn occurred. A lamb, calf or deer can quite quickly run along with its mother.

Common to all ruminants is that a great deal of resistance to local diseases is given to the animal via the colostrum and not via the blood. It is therefore of paramount importance that the young ruminant receives colostrum as soon after birth as possible. If a calf, lamb or kid is very weak at birth there is probably no better lifesaver than the giving of colostrum through a stomach tube. *Forcing the weak to suck or drink can often result in some of the liquids passing into the lungs, which can give rise to pneumonia and sometimes instant death (Fig. 1).*

FIGURE 1   **Colostrum should be given by stomach tube to avoid the risk of liquid entering the lungs**

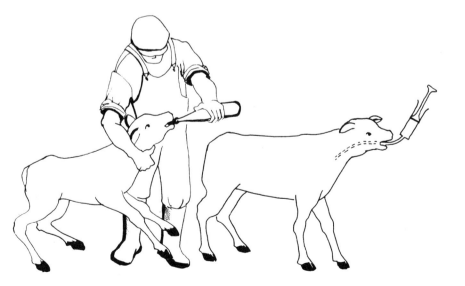

Nutrition of the newborn

Having made sure that the young animal has had colostrum, the stockman has then to make a choice of whether to wean it or leave it with its dam. This choice is strongly influenced by the type of the animal production. Milk producers will probably choose to wean the young as soon as possible, whether they be lambs, kids or calves,though for some species of domestic ruminant, such as cattle, it has been found an advantage to leave the young with their dams to ensure let down of milk. In fact, in some countries it has been found that leaving the calves with the cows for a few hours after milking increases both milk for sale and growth rates of the calves.

If the decision is to leave a young animal to suckle its dam there are relatively few decisions to be made, except regarding nutrition of the dam. *It is perhaps worth pointing out that, while a dairy cow can yield enough milk to feed 5 or 6 calves, which is quite impressive, a ewe feeding twin or triplet lambs often yields the same output of energy in milk for the lambs, relative to her body size, as a high-yielding Friesian cow (Fig. 2).* The consumption of milk energy by lambs relative to body weight is greater than that by calves. This can best be illustrated by considering that a growth rate of 500 g/d by lambs is quite possible in large breeds of sheep, while newborn calves seldom grow at a rate much greater than 1 kg/d. This comment is made only to emphasise to shepherds that ewes nursing two or more lambs need to be well fed if the growth rates of the lambs are to be sustained. Ewes, however much they deserve it, seldom get the attention that dairy cows do.

With multiple-suckled cows, frequent lambing systems and prolific ewe flocks there is always a problem of fostering, such as extra calves on dairy type suckler cows or extra lambs on ewes giving birth to single lambs. The methods of successful crossfostering are many and varied and need not be discussed here.

Artificial rearing

If it is decided that young animals are to be artificially reared then the advice is to remove them from their dams within about 24 h of birth. The reason for this will become clear later when particular behaviour patterns of young animals associated with drinking are discussed. If they are left with their dams, for whatever well intentioned reasons, behaviour patterns are established which become increasingly difficult to alter. Failure to develop the behaviour pattern appropriate to the drinking method chosen (bucket, trough or teat) can have serious repercussions on the animals' nutrition (see later).

FIGURE 2 **A ewe with triplets yields the same milk energy, relative to body size, as a high-yielding cow**

35 kg

It would be so much easier if the young ruminant from birth could be given dried milk powder and consume water *ad libitum*. While this may be possible with early weaned pigs, it is not possible with ruminants. This is due to the peculiar construction of the stomach, and therefore at this early stage in the book a special mention has to be made about the stomach of ruminants. *At birth the stomach is as shown in Fig. 3*; the rumen, which in mature life is the feed processor, is very small and non-functional. The true stomach, on the other hand, is well developed and equal to or even greater in size than the rumen. *In later life these proportions alter dramatically, the rumen attaining a size 10 times greater than the true stomach (Fig. 4).*

FIGURE 3 **At birth the abomasum or true stomach is well-developed**

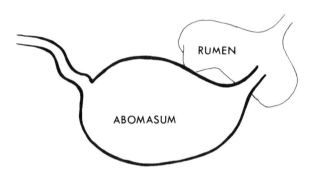

FIGURE 4 **In the mature ruminant the rumen is 10 times as large as the true stomach**

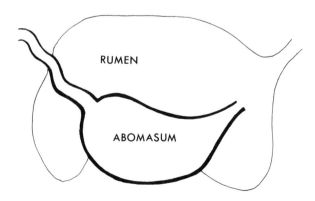

When the young animal drinks milk from its dam or from an artificial device such as a teat or bucket, the liquid is channelled directly into the true stomach by a very elegant mechanism known as the oesophageal groove. This is best understood by imagining that the rumen has developed from a slit in the oesophagus or gullet. If the slit is closed the oesophagus continues to the true stomach. If the slit is open, swallowed material falls through into the rumen. Solid food does not operate the mechanism and therefore enters the rumen, so even if the young after birth were able to consume solid milk replacers it would be nutritionally undesirable, as it would result in acid formation in the rumen and possibly bloat.

There is no choice as far as the form of the milk replacer for ruminants is concerned – it has to be liquid in order to nourish the young adequately (Fig. 5).

FIGURE 5 **Milk replacers for young ruminants should be liquid**

Training the young to drink from a rearing device

There are essentially two methods of providing milk substitute. The young animal either sucks milk substitute from a teat or it drinks from a trough or a bucket. The method chosen is generally the one which is most convenient and the newborn must be trained accordingly. *For small ruminants, such as lambs and kids, the more usual method is sucking from a teat, while with calves the most common method is the use of a bucket or trough (Fig. 6).* As a young animal instinctively sucks, a calf is generally trained to drink from a bucket by tempting it to suck on fingers immersed in the milk. The calf then discovers that sucking is not required and that the liquid can be sipped rather than sucked.

It is interesting to note that there are breeds of cattle where training calves to drink from a bucket is virtually impossible and teat feeding is almost essential. If difficulty is experienced in making the change from sucking to sipping it is better to use a teat fixed outside the bucket than to prolong training. The calf which never accepts sipping as a substitute for mother's teat is the calf that appears to drink not for pleasure but to please the stockman! It is normally a poor calf because the liquid given has entered the rumen and is therefore being poorly utilised due to the destructive action of bacteria.

FIGURE 6 **Lambs normally suck from a teat whilst calves are trained to drink from a bucket**

Until recently it was generally accepted that the actual composition of milk would trigger the closure of the oesophageal groove or slit so that the liquid entered directly into the true stomach. This has been disproved and the importance of the behaviour of the animal is emphasised. It is a well known phenomenon, taught in biology, that dogs will salivate on hearing a sound associated with feeding time. This phenomenon is called a conditioned reflex. The closure of the groove occurs in the same way. *In Fig. 7 it is shown that if liquid is given into the oesophagus it will enter the true stomach if the animal is expecting a drink from the bottle or bucket to which it has become accustomed, even if the liquid is not actually drunk but the oesophageal groove is closed. However, if the animal is not anticipating a feed because the person or the bottle are not seen, liquid will enter the rumen (Fig. 8).*

It is normally easy to recognise whether the groove closure is operating efficiently. A number of external signs such as tail wagging and head butting are good indications that milk is entering the true stomach (Fig. 9).

FIGURE 7 **The oesophageal groove can be closed by a conditioned reflex when the animal can see the person**

FIGURE 8 **Liquid can enter the rumen if the animal cannot see the person or the bottle**

FIGURE 9 **Tail wagging is a good indication that milk is entering the true stomach**

Composition of milk substitutes

The most common reason for artificial rearing is that the revenue from milk sold is greater than the cost of milk substitute. While whole milk powder is best for the animal, this is of course not economical. Generally the butter fat at least has been removed and the milk substitute is based on skimmed milk with a cheaper source of fat such as lard and tallow. In fact there are many other fractions of the milk substitute that can be changed besides the fat, but generally this is not economical. Replacement of the milk protein with other sources of protein is possible but is technically difficult to make and requires more care in feeding. The milk protein will form a large clot when it has reacted with stomach juices and this large clot is then gradually eroded. As a result twice daily feeding of milk becomes more like continuous feeding as it takes several hours for the milk clot to be digested. If the milk protein is replaced by other types of protein then no clot is formed and so it becomes necessary to feed the animals more frequently to avoid scouring.

Cow's milk normally contains less fat than ewe's milk and therefore milk substitute for lambs should generally contain more fat than milk substitute for calves.

Consumption of solid feed

In general solid feed, even in the form of good quality material, will not be consumed in any measurable quantity before calves, lambs or kids are about 2 weeks old. After that period young animals will eat increasing quantities of other feed but the amount eaten, apart from the obvious factor of availability, will depend on the amount of liquid milk received. If milk substitute is given then it is generally economical to make the young eat solid feed as soon as possible, because milk substitute will nearly always be more expensive than even the best quality solid feed, and much less work is involved in providing solid feed. There are also situations with young animals suckling their dams, that early weaning is advantageous, for instance with the frequent-breeding ewe. This will be discussed later.

Solid food on consumption enters the rumen and fermentation soon starts due to bacteria swallowed with the food. The fermentation of solid feed and the production of acids stimulates growth of the rumen and this in turn enables young animals to eat greater quantities of solid food. In order to speed up rumen development and thereby increase dependence on solid food it is necessary from the age of two weeks to reduce the quantities of liquid milk substitute offered, thereby stimulating increased consumption of solid feed. This means that growth rate will be less than the maximum growth rate. With good management and high quality solid feed calves, lambs and kids can all be weaned at 4 to 5 weeks of age. They will, however, sometimes suffer a growth check lasting maybe a week or two, and it is essential at this time that high quality feeds are freely available.

Feeding of milk substitute with solid feed

During the period when dry feed consumption is encouraged the routine of feeding milk substitutes should continue in the same manner, though the amount given may be reduced. However, one other aspect of management now becomes very important, which is that along with the desire to consume solid food comes the desire to drink liquid to quench thirst. This is very important since the motive of the animal to drink for thirst is entirely different from the motive to drink in a state of juvenile excitement. It is also important from a nutritional point of view because liquids drunk to assuage thirst will pass into the rumen. There is now a difficulty, particularly if the calves or lambs have been trained to sip milk from a bucket, because the animals will use the same method of drinking when they are thirsty. It is therefore possible to confuse the animals. For instance, if no water is offered along with solid food some of the milk given may be drunk for thirst and will thus be poorly utilized. *The only manageable solution is to ensure that water is freely available at all times and that the normal milk feeding routine is followed, in which case milk will not be consumed to quench thirst, but will continue to pass into the true stomach (Fig. 10).*

FIGURE 10 **Water should be freely available at all times**

Early weaning to solid feed

Since milk substitutes are expensive and the feeding of milk substitutes labour consuming, it is generally good economy to early-wean animals that are receiving milk substitutes. It was mentioned earlier that it was possible to wean animals at 4 to 5 weeks of age providing that good quality, digestible solid feed has been available to them and that the allowance of liquid milk substitutes has been reduced during the last couple of weeks before weaning.

Composition of feed after weaning

It is important to remember that the rumen, while rapidly developing, has not reached mature proportions when lambs, kids or calves are weaned at 4 to 5 weeks of age. In order to compensate for the small size of the rumen the feed must be of the kind that will be digested quickly, so that a greater amount of food can be consumed. This often means feeding large proportions of concentrate.

Most so-called concentrates are bought-in compound feeds but young animals can do well on such items as sugar beet pulp, brewers grains and even roots, which are perfectly satisfactory if they are cut into manageable pieces. Lightly rolled grain and, for small ruminants, whole grain can also be given. Hay and straw may be made available but in the early stages is not essential and should not be considered as providing nutrients. The required structure of the diet can be achieved by the use of lightly rolled or whole cereals.

A problem for the small ruminant in particular is that of the removal of indigestible particles from the rumen. For instance, oat husks will tend to stay for a long time in the rumen of kids and lambs because of the size of the husk relative to the size of the opening from the rumen downstream. As a result oats should not generally be given as a large part of the feed for small ruminants such as lambs and kids, but are excellent for young calves.

Protein requirements of early-weaned animals

The protein requirements of ruminants in general will be dealt with later. It is only necessary to stress here that when animals are weaned early they are also deprived of milk protein which, as mentioned earlier, enters the true stomach directly. The protein requirement of young animals is high because they deposit a lot of lean tissue rather than fat. In nature, young animals are weaned at a stage when their protein requirement is relatively lower. For early-weaned animals this must be compensated by the protein supplement in the diet. The protein used should also be of the kind that the bacteria in the rumen will not destroy. Animal protein such as fishmeal, meat and bone meal and bloodmeal are useful in this respect. Of the vegetable proteins, linseed meal is one of the best. This will be dealt with in more detail in a later chapter.

Feeding protein supplements via the oesophageal groove

It was mentioned earlier that the most important point about the proper functioning of the oesophageal groove is not the composition of the milk substitutes, the method of drinking (teat, trough or bucket), nor the height of the drinking device, but the behaviour of the animal. As a result, it is in fact quite possible to change from milk substitutes to protein suspensions while continuing to operate the oesophageal groove mechanism, which ensures that the protein escapes destruction in the rumen. In many countries it is generally felt that the additional labour required in continuous liquid feeding is not justified by the benefit. On the other hand, it may well be that with some calf rearing systems it would be desirable, particularly in countries where there is plenty of cheap labour. In Asia this method has created a great deal of interest. It should also be pointed out that automatic dispensers of liquid may become increasingly used, and this in turn may enable us to feed protein suspensions, thus achieving a better utilization of protein for our growing ruminants.

Late weaning to solid feed

In systems of late weaning (which applies to most sheep, suckler cow and suckler goat systems) the young are generally weaned when their stomachs have reached mature proportions, at around 4 to 5 months of age. This means that many options are available, many different feeds can be used, and furthermore, their protein requirement is generally that which can be supplied as bacterial cells formed during the fermentation of the feeds.

CHAPTER 2

THE FERMENTATION IN THE RUMEN

In this Chapter the principles of fermentation in the rumen will be discussed in some detail. An understanding of rumen fermentation will help the stockman to avoid many expensive mistakes in veterinary bills and sometimes dead animals.

The rumen fermentation can be compared with wine making. There are many ways of making good wine but some principles are common to all. The amateur winemaker has normally perhaps 2 or 3 fermenters operating and normally the yeast organisms are similar. In the rumen there is a multitude of types of bacteria, each performing different functions so that complex carbohydrates can be converted to organic acids which the host animal can utilize. *Bacteria adhere to particles of roughage and gradually erode out the digestible material (Fig. 11).*The farmer in a way is responsible for as many complex fermentation chambers as he has ruminants on his farm.

FIGURE 11   **Bacteria adhere to feed particles in the rumen and erode the digestible material** *Photo: Rowett Research Institute*

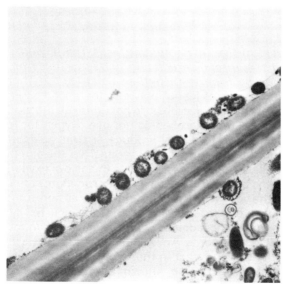

Principles of fermentation

The ruminant evolved to ferment its feed with the help of microorganisms. This is an excellent choice for cellulosic materials such as grass, hay, silage and straw since the animal itself cannot break down cellulose to a form it can utilize. Fermentation is not a particularly good choice when the ruminant eats concentrate, since fermentation involves losses of energy and the animal could digest starch without fermenting it first.

FIGURE 12   **Fermentation in the rumen involves loss of energy as methane gas**

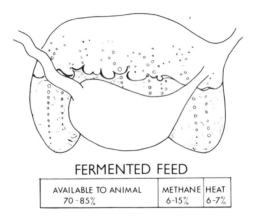

FERMENTED FEED

AVAILABLE TO ANIMAL 70 - 85%	METHANE 6-15%	HEAT 6 -7%

There is a cost involved in fermenting feeds. This is seen in losses of gas, mainly methane, through eructation, and some heat from fermentation itself that must be dispersed of by the animal (Fig. 12). There is, however, an excellent division of labour between the microbes and the animal, which ensures that the microbes do not utilize all the feed. This is made possible because the microbes do not use oxygen for fermenting the feed. They can therefore only produce organic acids such as acetic, propionic and butyric acids. The host animal (i.e. the animal itself) in turn absorbs the acids and utilizes them with the help of oxygen. This is a very important principle. The net result is that a ruminant cannot convert feed to energy in the body with the same efficiency as non-ruminants such as pigs and poultry, due to losses in gas and heat incurred by the microbes. On the other hand, most domestic non-ruminants cannot use cellulosic feeds as well as ruminants. Any cellulose they do use is also fermented, at the other end of the tract in the large intestine. These two types of digestive systems are also known as forestomach and hind gut fermentation. The horse is an excellent example of an efficient hind gut fermenter.

16

Advantages and disadvantages of forestomach and hind gut fermentation

The advantages for forestomach fermentation are that the size of the stomach allows a relatively long residence time for the feed in the stomach, so that feeds which ferment slowly can be utilized; the second and, possibly, more important advantage is that the microbial cells which have grown as a result of fermenting feeds in the rumen consist, to a large extent, of protein which then flows into the true stomach along with liquid and small particles and is the most important source of protein for ruminants. In effect the animal's reward to the microbes for their service in making feed available to it is to digest them afterwards!

The main disadvantage of forestomach fermentation is that feeds which do not need to be fermented, such as starch in cereals, are fermented all the same and some energy is lost unnecessarily. Forestomach fermentation has also, as will be discussed later, some disadvantages as far as protein feeding is concerned. The microbes not only ferment cellulose and starch; they also ferment protein.The fermentation of protein in fact yields less bacterial protein than that which results from the fermentation of an equal amount of protein-free cellulose or starch. The long residence time is dictated to the ruminant partly through the size of the outlet from the rumen down to the true stomach. This is called the reticulo-omasal orifice,and can have the disadvantage that a great deal of chewing and rumination is required before some particles of feed are small enough to escape.

The great advantage of hind gut fermentation is that those parts of the feed which suffer unnecessary losses in nutritive value through fermentation are digested normally and only the material which cannot be digested directly is exposed to fermentation in the hind gut.

The main disadvantage of hind gut fermentation, particularly if the largest part of the diet is cellulose material, is that the bacterial cells formed are excreted in the dung and not digested. *The rabbit, however, clearly organizes its lifestyle correctly and overcomes this problem by eating a great deal of its dung, 'the soft faeces' (Fig. 13)*, and thus obtains all the advantages of fermentation. The other major disadvantage is that the hind gut is not normally large enough to allow a high residence time so that the digestibility of cellulose feeds, e.g. hay, silage, etc., among hindgut fermenters is almost invariably lower than in ruminants. The low residence time may however be an advantage. For instance horses grazing poor pastures can, due to large throughput but low digestibility, sometimes gain weight whereas ruminants, due to the long residence time and lower intake of food, lose weight in spite of achieving a higher digestibility.

FIGURE 13 The rabbit overcomes the disadvantages of hind gut fermentation by eating its soft faeces

Speed of fermentation of different feeds

It is well known that feeds vary in digestibility or in Metabolisable Energy (ME) value (generally calculated from an estimated digestibility). However, it is probably not so well known that the time taken to ferment the digestible part of the feed also varies enormously. Table 2.1 shows some approximate values of the speed of digestion of some common feedstuffs.

TABLE 2.1 Digestibility and Speed of Digestion of Common Feeds

	Digestibility (%)	Speed of digestion (hours)
Molasses	95	0.5
Beet and turnips	85	2 to 6
Cereals	80	12 to 14
Good grass	70	18 to 24
Good clover	70	12 to 18
Poor hay	55	30 to 40
Straw	40	45 to 55

It can be seen that, on the whole, the lower the digestibility the longer it takes for the digestible material to ferment. The speed at which different parts of a feed ferments also varies. For instance, grass contains a sugar-like material equally soluble to molasses and which ferments equally rapidly.

These differences in speed of digestion are very important when we attempt to understand feed intake in ruminants. A further disadvantage for low digestibility feeds such as straw is that the lower the digestibility the greater the indigestible residue. The indigestible part of straw that the animal has to get rid of is generally also tougher and requires more chewing and rumination than the indigestible part of good grass. This further increases the residence time of straw in the rumen and causes a greater limitation to the amount of material that the animal can consume.

Fermentation of different feed constituents

Before proceeding to discuss feeds, it is useful to consider the fermentation of the most important components of feeds.

Cellulose

This is the most important nutrient in ruminant feeds, e.g. grass, hay, silage and straw and stalks. It is the ability efficiently to digest cellulose that characterizes ruminants and will no doubt ensure their survival since they do not compete for human food.

Cellulose on its own is completely digestible although it does not ferment as fast as starch and sugars. The reason why cellulosic feeds are often of low digestibility is due to a compound known as lignin, which protects cellulose from bacterial invasion and acts as binding material. In fact the material which ensures that hay and straw can stand up straight and carry a seedhead is also the material which in general limits both the speed of digestion and the amount of digestion possible. It does not seem possible to have a highly digestible cellulose structure carrying a large seedhead. This can also be illustrated by the fact that cellulose in leaves is generally more digestible than cellulose in stems.

From a practical nutritional point of view there are three aspects of cellulose fermentation that should be known and understood by the farmer:

* Cellulose fermenting bacteria are very sensitive to excess acidity. They function best at a rumen pH of 6.4 to 7.0. Their growth rate is already slowing down if the pH falls to 6.2 and is completely stopped at a pH of less than 6.0. This is very important when considering how best to combine different feeds.

* Cellulose fermenting bacteria produce a large proportion of acetic acid. This aspect of cellulose digestion is important in the production of milk fat.

* Cellulose fermenting bacteria are sensitive to fats. If the feed contains too much fat the cellulose bacteria can also be completely eliminated or slowed down in growth rate. This is important as sometimes over-feeding of fat can reduce both intake of cellulosic feeds and also their digestibility.

Starch

Starch is the main ingredient in cereals, potatoes and some tropical root crops such as cassava. The bacteria fermenting starch are distinctly different from the bacteria fermenting cellulose. Unlike cellulose-fermenting bacteria starch fermenters are quite insensitive to acidity. They ferment starch equally well at pH 5.5 as at pH 7. At a very low pH or at a pH less than about 5.5 only a few types can survive. One type produces lactic acid, while other types ferment lactic acid further to propionic acid. If the bacteria which utilize lactic acid are not present in sufficient numbers, for example if cereals are fed to animals that are not adapted to them, then lactic acid can accumulate. If large amounts of lactic acid are absorbed then we have problems of acidosis, which at worst can be fatal, or at best put the animals off feed for several days.

Bacteria fermenting starch produce mainly propionic acid, which is important since an excessive production of propionic acid reduces butterfat in milk.

Sugars

Some bacteria which ferment sugars are very similar to those fermenting starch. The feeds containing large amounts of sugars are molasses, fodder beet and turnips, but grass and good hay also contain a considerable amount. On the whole sugars in grass and root crops are not eaten as fast as starchy feeds and therefore there are generally fewer problems of acidosis. Molasses is normally licked and the sugar from roots is consumed more slowly since roots contain up to 80 or 90% water. While bacteria fermenting sugars produce mainly propionic acid, they can also produce large proportions of butyric acid which tends to increase the butterfat percentage in milk.

Protein

Many bacteria, including those fermenting cellulose, starch and sugars, will also ferment protein. Although fermentation of protein also provides the bacteria with energy without utilising oxygen, this is a very small amount compared to the energy they can get from carbohydrates such as sugar, starch and cellulose. Fermentation of protein yields ammonia and a mixture of organic acids. The ammonia can be used by the bacteria to form new protein in their cells. However, the bacteria do not limit themselves to the break down of protein only to give them enough ammonia. They break down as much protein as they can during the time available. *Since bacterial growth is generally limited by the energy available from carbohydrates in the absence of oxygen, ammonia in excess of their requirements cannot be utilized by them. The excess ammonia is absorbed by the animal and appears in the urine as urea. There may also be a deficit which slows down digestion in the rumen and reduces feed intake (Fig. 14).*

FIGURE 14   **The breakdown of protein by bacteria in the rumen yields ammonia. The rate of ammonia release should match as closely as possible the release of energy**

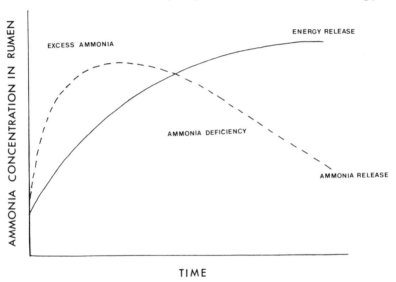

Combining feeds together

In most ruminant production systems more than one type of feed is given, and this is where the skill in feeding ruminants really counts. Feeding the right combinations of feeds in the correct manner can easily cause improvements in feed utilization of 10 to 20%. It can avoid many problems of feed intake and can in effect mean loss or profit to the farmer. Apart from problems of acidosis, which generally result from feeding starchy concentrates in large quantities before the appropriate

21

microflora have developed adequately, most of the problems of feed combinations arise when feed containing mainly cellulose is mixed with feed containing mainly starch or soluble sugars. It was mentioned earlier that starch or soluble sugar fermenting bacteria are not very sensitive to acidity in the rumen, while cellulose digesting bacteria are very sensitive to a low rumen pH (less than 6.2).

Controlling acidity in the rumen

Before further discussion of the combinations of feeds it is appropriate to explain how the animal attempts to create the best condition for its workers, the rumen microflora. As discussed before, the ruminant animal has evolved a system to digest cellulose efficiently, thus the animal attempts to maintain optimal conditions for cellulose digestion.

The animal controls rumen acidity by secreting saliva, during eating and rumination, which is alkaline and neutralises the acids present and formed in the rumen. *The quantity of saliva secreted depends largely on the length of time spent eating and ruminating as this is the time when saliva production is greatest. The amount of acid produced from fermentation is directly proportional to the digestibility of the feed. Thus only about half the acids are produced from fermenting straw compared to the same weight of cereals. This is, in a nutshell, the greatest problem in combining cellulosic materials with soluble starch and sugars (Fig. 15).* Because the feeding of concentrate requires less chewing and rumination time, the ruminant produces less saliva per unit weight of cereals than of straw; ideally it should produce more.

FIGURE 15   **Equal weights of straw and cereals occupy greatly different volumes. More saliva and less acid are produced from straw than from cereals**

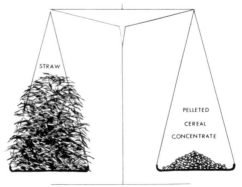

The resultant effect is that if rolled or ground cereals are fed as the only feed for steers or lambs, the rumen pH will stabilize at about 5.2 to 5.4. When straw, or poor-to-medium quality hay is fed, the rumen pH stabilizes at about 6.8 to 7.0.

Level of feeding

Since there is always a certain amount of saliva produced whether the animals eat or not, the proportion of rapidly fermenting feeds that can be included in a diet before interfering with the digestion of cellulose depends very much on the total quantity of feed given, i.e. on the feeding level. The greater the feeding level, the greater the problem. In other words, the minimum proportion of concentrate which can be tolerated depends on the amount fed. For dairy cows consuming a large amount of feed, the problem is greatest of all. It is not possible to say with a great deal of accuracy how high the proportion of concentrate can be in a diet because that depends on other factors as well as feeding level. The only advice that can be safely given is that if the acidity of the rumen fluid is such that pH is less than about 6.2, then cellulose digestion is less than optimal. The depression in digestibility and intake that occurs as a result depends on the length of time during the 24 h day that the pH in the rumen is below 6.2.

Processing of cereals

It is possible to manipulate the speed at which cereals are fermented by the degree of processing. The optimum amount of processing is that which gives acceptable and close to maximal digestibility. Further processing will only cause additional interference with digestion. For sheep, as will be discussed later, the optimum processing of cereals is not to process at all. For cattle, the minimum processing is also the optimum. Crimping, or light rolling or simply treatment with caustic soda at harvesting is adequate. Pelleting of cereal-based concentrate also adds to the problems of digestion if the pellets are fed in combination with roughage diets, and pelleting generally adds to the cost.

It has already been mentioned that the degree of processing of cereals can have marked effects on rumen pH. In particular, feeding whole grain to sheep increases the time taken eating and ruminating and thereby increases saliva production. As a result there is a higher pH and less interference with cellulose digestion in the rumen.

Addition of sodium bicarbonate

The alkalinity of saliva is mainly due to sodium bicarbonate and therefore it is obvious to think of increasing 'saliva production' by adding it to the diet. Sodium bicarbonate can indeed help to restore the digestibility of roughage to normal and can also, in the milking animal, restore milk fat to normal because of increased cellulose digestion and thus acetic acid production. In some dietary situations in which a large proportion of starchy concentrate is given, particularly to cows, then sodium bicarbonate can help to reduce the problem, but the higher the feeding level the more difficult the solution, since so much bicarbonate has to be included that the feed becomes unpalatable.

Frequent feeding

If there are likely to be problems in the feeding of large proportions of concentrate then they can be overcome by increasing the frequency with which the concentrate is fed. Electronic control of the quantity consumed at each feed helps to cut down the labour requirement in the management of this principle. Before this is discussed in detail it is useful to describe what happens to acidity in the rumen in relation to feeding times of concentrate. The change in rumen pH is illustrated in Fig. 16a and b; (a) where concentrate constitutes a large proportion of the ration - about 60 to 70% is common in dairy cows fed in some countries and (b) where concentrate is only 30 to 40% of the total feed − commonly found with dry and low yielding cows, and also in some beef and sheep production systems.

When concentrate is given twice daily, the greatest acidity or lowest pH is reached 2-3 hours after feeding for both levels of concentrate illustrated in figure 18. If the concentrate is given in a completely mixed diet the acidity is reasonably stable. There will be variation due to the pattern of eating. The animals do not eat all the time even though feed is available all the time. *With a low level concentrate it can be seen that for twice daily feeding of concentrate the acidity increases to the extent that the cellulose digestion is inhibited (as mentioned earlier at pH less than about 6.2) for only a short period after feeding (Fig. 16a).* So the twice daily pattern of feeding is likely to cause some depression in intake and digestion of the roughage. There is no problem with a completely mixed diet.

With a high level of concentrate it can be seen that with twice daily feeding, the pH is depressed for longer after feeding but recovers for a period between feeds to a level where cellulose is fermented. But there is hardly any recovery with the completely mixed diet (Fig. 16b) and although the rumen pH is stable, there will be very little digestion of cellulose. In other words, completely mixed diets are not always the best solution for optimum digestion. The best solution is when the proportion of concentrate does not exceed about 50% of the diet, depending on type of concentrate and the level of feeding. Other problems such as acidosis may be more prevalent with once or twice daily feeding of concentrate so complete diet feeding may still be the preferred solution, even though digestibility is not optimal.

FIGURE 16   It is important to prevent the pH of the rumen from falling below 6.0 for long periods of time, otherwise cellulose digestion will be greatly reduced. The problem is less at low levels of concentrate feeding (16a) than at high levels (16b)

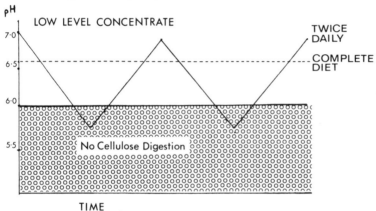

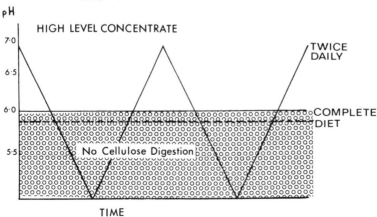

What is a concentrate?

The word concentrate is often used without a clear understanding of what it means. Some farmers use the term concentrate for bought-in, processed compound feeds, other farmers include home-grown grain in this term. As far as fermentation is concerned it is preferable to define concentrate as non-cellulosic or low-cellulosic carbohydrate. However, if this is done then this definition must include such feeds as roots like turnips, fodder beet and swedes, and tubers like potatoes; it must also be concluded that products such as brewer's yeast, sugar beet pulp and many by-products included in compounds are not concentrates. In fact, farmers must increasingly accept that roots have characteristics similar to starchy feeds. They ferment rapidly. However, they do not (or very seldom) cause problems of very low acidity because their dry matter must, by their physical nature, be consumed slowly. This has the dual effect of resulting in relatively slow speed of fermentation in the rumen and also of increasing the amount of saliva being produced, which helps to reduce acidity in the rumen, remembering that saliva production increases with an increased period of eating.

In practice, therefore, roots should be considered on a par with cereals except that they are relatively safer to feed. However they still inhibit the digestion of cellulose in a similar way to grain and can cause acidosis by too sudden an introduction - sudden access of cows to fields of root crops can be fatal!

The definition of concentrate is particularly important in the feeding of dairy cows, where a high level is usually given. It would be advisable to change to a greater proportion of by-products such as sugar beet pulp or brewers grain, as the proportion of concentrate is increasing. A recent trial at the Rowett Research Institute showed for instance that ammonia-treated straw, sugar beet pulp and rolled barley had digestibilities of 54, 83 and 83 respectively when fed alone. Combining straw at 30% and sugar beet pulp at 70% gave a digestibility of 70% while the same proportion of straw with rolled barley was only 65% digestible. It could be calculated that while the digestibility of straw was reduced to 44% with sugar beet pulp it was only 22% when combined with barley.

If bicarbonate is mixed well with the feed then the animals will eat the feed, and, due to the resulting increase in cellulose digestion, the feeding of bicarbonate can sometimes increase feed intake. Bicarbonate will not be consumed by the animals unless it forms part of the feed.

Another method of increasing alkali intake to counteract acidity is to use sodium hydroxide as the method of preserving high moisture grains. The sodium hydroxide takes up carbon-dioxide from the air and becomes carbonate. Thus the caustic soda, apart from having the effect of preserving and processing grain, can also assist in the overall digestion of cellulose.

Consequences of acidity in the rumen

In almost all cases, when cellulose digestion is less than optimal there will be a reduction in the digestibility, or in the true ME value. This is serious in feed evaluation systems which normally assume that combinations of feeds are used in an additive manner, i.e. that two feeds fed together give the same value as the sum of individual feeds. The reason for this assumption is due to the fact that the effect of combinations of cereals and other feeds have been studied mainly at the maintenance level of feeding. As a result the animals are in effect given less than the calculated requirement for feed and their performance may not meet expectations.

The extent to which digestibility is depressed depends on the physical state of the roughage. If the fibre is ground and pelleted, digestibility may on occasions be almost halved because the particles can pass out of the rumen rapidly, although the fibre could have been fermented if it had remained for long enough. The depression is less, but can easily still be 20% or more, with long particles, e.g. silage, hay and straw. *In Fig. 17 the effect of feeding different proportions of concentrate on the digestion of hay in the rumen is illustrated. The speed at which the bacteria ferment cellulose is slowed down in the presence of concentrate. The depression in feed intake of roughage as a result of concentrate feeding is greatest with long roughage and also as a general rule greatest with poor quality roughages.* In fact the reduction in intake of roughage when concentrate is given in increasing amounts is sometimes equal to the amount of supplement fed. In this case the intended supplementation of feed becomes a substitution which is not only undesirable and unwanted, but generally uneconomical, as the supplementary feed of concentrate is more expensive than the roughage it replaces. In practice it often takes time to discover this is happening because the animals have *ad libitum* access to roughage, so lower intakes may not be noticed until the animals prove to have a poor feed utilization.

For the milking animal the effect of reduced intake and digestibility of roughage also has the effect of reducing acetic acid production and, as will be shown later, this can reduce the butterfat content and thus the price received for milk.

FIGURE 17   **The speed of digestion of hay is reduced when concentrates are included in the diet**

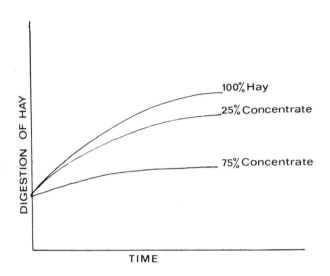

Changing from fibrous to concentrate feeds or vice versa

By far the greatest number of fatalities due to the inappropriate management of ruminant feeding occur when a change in the diet is made. A change in the diet for simple-stomached animals like pigs, and indeed ourselves, is relatively harmless – a sudden change in diet for ruminants can be fatal. The amateur winemaker will be easy to convince about this because he understands that an uncontrolled change will mean a change in the microbes. The most dangerous change is the one from a high roughage fermentation to a high concentrate one. Such changes can occur accidentally, like ruminants getting access to a field of sugar beet, or access to grain. Perhaps more often the problem occurs out of kindness in the belief that dairy cows, in particular, must receive generous rations of concentrate as quickly as possible after calving. On the Continent 'sweet breath' or 'acetonaemia' is called 'small-holders disease' – referring to the kind attention given to the cows. The lactic acid which accumulates, because the bacteria normally using it are not there, causes the syndrome of acidosis. In dairy cows this is normally followed by sweet breath or acetonaemia which occurs when the animals stop eating but continue to give milk.

28

One of the particular problems of changing to high concentrate feeding is the inability to measure the amount of roughage that the animals eat. It is possible that the animals are eating much less roughage than is expected so the proportion of concentrate is in effect altered more quickly than anticipated. A change must be made very gradually often over a period of 2 to 3 weeks to avoid problems. The quantity of concentrate given at any one time, the degree to which the concentrate is processed, and the frequency of feeding are all factors which affect the time necessary to effect a change in feeding. The total level of feeding is also very important. It is only when, for instance, the animals are being given a maintenance feed that a rapid change can be tolerated because the acidity in the rumen will not be affected to the extent which would occur at a much higher level of feeding.

A change from a high concentrate to a high cellulosic diet is much easier, or at least it is not dangerous and can be made over a shorter period of time. The change will give a lower than expected intake of roughage during the first week or two therefore, although the change can be made more abruptly, it is preferable to spread it over a period of a few days.

How to achieve the maximum digestion of different feeds

First of all, the assumption must be made that optimum digestion is necessarily also the most economic way of feeding. Many other considerations have to be made when economics are considered including feeding level, interest rates, turnover rates, capital, etc. Here we are concerned only with optimum utilization from a dietary point of view.

It was mentioned earlier that cellulose digestion is easily inhibited when too much concentrate is fed, due mainly to a high acidity in the rumen. If, therefore, a high cellulosic diet based on straw, hay, silage, grass or other cellulose by-products is given, then the most efficient digestion occurs with little, if any, concentrate. The amount of concentrate (the definition of which was discussed earlier) that can be tolerated depends on the type of concentrate and the chosen level of feeding. If the animals are only fed a maintenance diet then cellulose digestion is not disturbed by up to at least 50% concentrate. If the feeding level is higher, then less concentrate can be used before cellulose digestion is below maximum.

As far as the digestion of starch and other soluble sugars (such as molasses) is concerned, the acidity in the rumen is not very important for complete digestion. The limitation here is the health of the animal itself. *Some roughage or structure in the diet is beneficial in increasing the production of saliva and maintaining the acidity in the rumen above danger level (Fig. 18a). If the pH falls to 5.4 or less then the lining of the rumen is damaged so that the rumen wall becomes inflamed and thickened (Fig. 18b). Cattle given diets deficient in long fibre often resort to licking each other. Hairs swallowed during licking become embedded in the thick and inflamed rumen wall, penetrate the wall and thus allow bacterial invasion of the blood, causing the well-known liver abcesses which are often found in cattle fattened on concentrate diets (Fig. 18c).*

FIGURE 18   **Inadequate long fibre in the diets can result in the lining of the rumen change from its normal appearance (a) to being thickened (b). Hairs swallowed during licking may become embedded in the rumen wall (c) allowing bacteria to infect the blood, causing liver abcesses.** *Photos: Rowett Research Institute.*

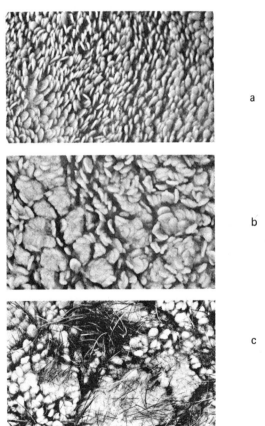

a

b

c

CHAPTER 3

FEED INTAKE

This chapter is devoted to feed intake because it is one of the most important aspects of ruminant nutrition. The amount of feed the animal can consume, both poor quality and high quality, determines productivity, or the amount of feed than can be used to produce animal products over and above that needed to maintain body functions and body weight.

Concentrates

If ruminant livestock are fattened on mainly cereal diets, the factors regulating how much the animal will eat are largely determined by the animal itself and its capacity to metabolize nutrients. This capacity depends on the age and weight of the animal and its stage of growth, breed and sex. Large breeds will usually eat more relative to body weight than small breeds; males will normally eat more than females. In short, feed intake is determined by the capacity of the animal to metabolize nutrients, in a similar way to the regulation of feed intake in single-stomached animals such as pigs and poultry. *The size of the rumen poses no limitation to intake. This is illustrated in Fig. 19.*

It is wrong, however, to think about ruminants being like single-stomach animals. When cereals are given, pigs and poultry digest starch and absorb glucose. Ruminants, in contrast, ferment starch in the rumen and absorb volatile fatty acids.

Roughages

The regulation of intake of roughages, in particular fibrous feeds such as straws is more complicated. *Here the stomach volume normally restricts the intake of feed so that the animal eats less than its capacity to utilize nutrients (Fig. 19).* There is, in other words, a physical restriction to feed consumption because the food ferments slowly and must, by nature of its particle size, stay in the rumen for a considerable time until the particles which are not digestible are small enough to pass out of the rumen. Assuming that essential nutrients such as protein are supplied to the microbes, there are essentially three very important attributes of the feed and one animal factor which all combine to determine the amount of poor quality roughage that can be consumed. The three feed factors are:

- Speed of digestion

- Digestibility

- Speed of reduction in particle size

The animal factor is gut capacity.

FIGURE 19   The size of the rumen poses no limitation to intake on high concentrate diets (a) but it does on diets high in roughage (b)

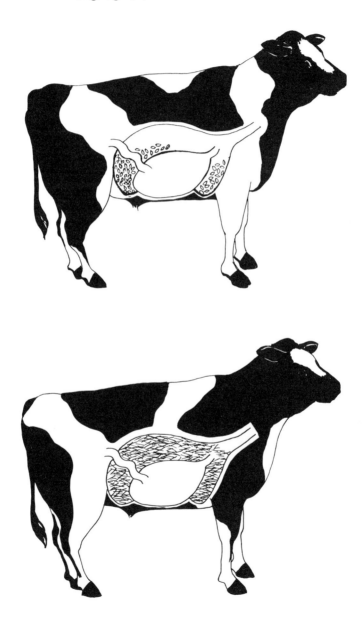

Speed of digestion

The speed of digestion is important because it determines the length of time that the digestible portion occupies space in the gut.

For almost all fibrous roughages such as hay, silage, or straw, there is a variable fraction of soluble sugars which ferments very quickly. In silage some of this portion is fermented to acids in the silo; and amounts in total to about 8 to 12% in straw and up to 40% in good quality grass. It is no wonder therefore that intake varies with the amount of soluble materials in the roughage because the soluble material occupies next to no space in the rumen.

However it must not be forgotten that the soluble material has effects on fibre digestion similar to concentrates, as discussed in Chapter 2. This means that too much soluble material can cause problems for fibre digestion. If the soluble material assisted digestion then molasses could be sprayed onto feeds such as straw to improve their value. In such cases the molasses can be utilized, but it does not help fibre digestion and can, given in large quantities, inhibit it.

The speed of digestion normally increases with increasing quality or digestibility but this is a general rule and there are many exceptions. For instance, clover with the same digestibility as grass will ferment faster, thus the animals will normally eat more clover than grass. *Fig. 20 represents three feeds with the same potential digestibility but with different speeds of digestion. The animals will eat most of feed 1 and least of feed 3.*

FIGURE 20   **Three feeds with the same potential digestibility but different speeds of digestion. The animal will eat most of feed 1 and least of feed 3**

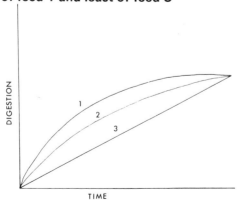

It is normal practice for farmers to consider roots like turnips, carrots or potatoes as roughages. As previously discussed this is not really correct as far as the microbes in the rumen are concerned. The animals can eat colossal amounts of roots but they will eat still more dry matter from concentrates. The intake of roots is somewhat limited by the speed at which the water and soluble sugars leave the cells and the speed at which the succulent pieces are masticated. The speed of digestion of roots themselves therefore depends on the rate of consumption of the root dry matter and the speed of fermentation. The sugars released from the roots can also have an effect on fibre digestion.

Digestibility

The digestibility of a feed determines the amount of undigested material that must pass out of the gut. As a general rule within a particular type of roughage the more digestible it is the more the animal can eat. It would seem more reasonable if it were the other way round, so that the animal could compensate for a feed low in digestibility by eating more of it.

The digestibility, or more precisely the indigestibility, of a feed determines the amount of feed residue that is occupying space in the rumen, i.e. in a way, occupying space for no useful purpose. The greater the amount of indigestible material, and the lower the speed at which the digestible part ferments, the more space is required for each unit of digestible energy, and consequently the animal is forced to eat less. As already discussed, if the speed of digestion is less than optimal due to interference with fibre digestion then digestibility will normally decrease as well. It is no surprise therefore that interference with digestion of fibre can have a dramatic effect on the amount the animal can eat.

Speed of reduction in particle size

The speed at which the indigestible portion is broken to particles small enough to pass through the small opening from the rumen into the lower stomach also influences intake. This aspect of the feed is not at all well understood, mainly because measurement of particle size is difficult. There are, however, large differences between feeds in this respect, mature grasses and straw being more tough than grass at an early stage. In addition, animal factors, particularly with regard to chewing, are also involved.

It would be easy to come to the conclusion that this was the most limiting factor to intake, because it determines the time taken for the indigestible particles to break down to particles which can escape out of the rumen. If this were the case then grinding of the roughage would solve the problem. Grinding certainly removes the limiting factor of particle size but results in the digestibility being below potential. If grinding was a cheap method of preparing fibrous feeds then it might be advantageous but on the whole it is too expensive for the gains possible. Any advantage of grinding is likely to be greatest for small ruminants such as sheep and calves, because the smaller the animal the smaller the particles on the whole must be before they can leave the rumen.

Gut capacity of the animal

The potential rumen volume determines the amount of feed the animal can ferment at any one time.

As discussed in Chapter 1 the rumen has not reached mature proportions before the animal is about 10 to 12 weeks old. Therefore the animal's capacity to eat fibrous roughage is less before that age is reached. In other words it is advisable to use the best quality roughage for young ruminants.

The gut capacities of mature ruminants differ, as can be observed in practice by the physical appearance of animals with large guts and also from the enormous amounts that some animals, notably large dairy cows, can consume.

The appearance of a large gut however has not always been an advantage particularly in the case of beef cattle, since they normally give a low killing out percentage. It is thus possible that, in the U.K. at least, there may have been selection against the ability of cattle to consume large amounts of roughage simply because a high killing out percentage has been a positive factor in selection.

There are still animal factors of gut capacity which are inadequately understood. Dry cows will not consume as much roughage as lactating cows, yet both would be subject to similar physical limitations on intake. Thus the animal with a very high need and capacity to metabolize nutrients appears to have an ability to eat more than the animal which needs less.

Cattle in northern Europe have apparently not the same capacity to consume roughage as cattle in South East Asia, where rice straw has been the staple feed and almost the only diet for centuries. It is important to examine this aspect when cattle breeds are exported to areas where resources are different. It may well be one reason for many disappointing cross-breeding attempts with native cattle in less developed countries. Whether the diets on which calves are reared will affect their ability to consume roughages in mature life is inadequately known. It is known however that overfatness and particularly the latter part of pregnancy can reduce abdominal volume and restrict the size of the gut.

Palatability

Finally there is also palatability itself; some plants are less liked by ruminants than others and sometimes plants eaten willingly by cows are rejected by sheep or *vice versa*. Often palatability has been confused with problems of speed of digestion, digestibility and reduction in size of long tough particles.

Prediction of intake

It is no surprise that the intake of a roughage is extremely difficult to predict. Two of the most important factors, namely the speed of digestion and the speed at which large particles are reduced in size are not described, nor is there as yet an adequate technique with which to do so. Only digestibility can be measured with any certainty and that is usually measured at the maintenance level of feeding, which may be of limited relevance. We need to be able to describe feeds in terms of their potential digestibility, the speed of digestion and the amount of soluble material they contain. Only then will the information provide some estimate of how much the animal can consume.

There is also inadequate knowledge about the capacity of animals to consume fibrous feeds and whether there are large differences between individuals within a breed or between breeds. A better understanding is required of the effect of feed intake, fatness and pregnancy on gut volume.

CHAPTER 4

ENERGY REQUIREMENTS

It is not easy to separate requirements for energy and for protein, but this will be explained in more detail when protein requirements are discussed.

Maintenance

Animals require energy for maintenance of body functions, temperature control, and production. The concept of maintenance requirement is often used to express level of feeding, for example, dairy cows at peak lactation can consume 3 to 4 times their requirement for maintenance.

If animals are fed below maintenance then they utilize body fat, which indeed may not be an uneconomical thing to do. Stored energy is like stored feed and if there is no body fat to utilize then of course the animals will die if no feed is given. This may seem logical, but losing and gaining weight is much more common than continually gaining weight, due to large seasonal fluctuations in feed supply in many countries. As will be discussed later, when animals receive inadequate feed energy to meet their maintenance requirements then protein will generally also be in short supply and weight loss will increase. Giving additional protein during periods of low level nutrition may be of great value in some areas, as it would prevent large losses of weight.

On the other hand, it is important to avoid overfat animals which are more likely to be rejected by the market. It is possible to reduce fatness without loss of lean by feeding low energy feeds such as straw with a small amount of protein which is not completely destroyed by the rumen microbes, e.g. fishmeal.

Requirements for growth depend on the composition of the tissues laid down. Lean tissues contain about 80% water and water contains no energy, so many different published values can easily be found for energy requirements for growth. It is more appropriate to think about requirements for increases in energy in the body, since the values will be more similar. In fact the energy cost of depositing energy in lean tissue is greater than the energy cost of depositing energy in fat. As a result the energy required per unit of energy increase in the body changes depending on the proportion of fat and protein in the body change. On the other hand the energy required for weight gain increases as the fat in the gain increases, since fat contains very little water and more energy than protein.

In fact the energy density in a unit of body weight can vary up to 8-fold. In practice the term feed conversion is often used. This is the amount of feed or dry matter required per unit of weight gain in the animal and the term has to be treated very carefully. Feed conversion will be lowest in animals laying down lean tissues – young lambs, calves and bulls – and greatest in animals laying down fat. At high feeding levels the amounts of cereals required per kg weight gain vary from less than 2 kg in very young ruminants to up to 10 kg in older ruminants laying down fat. However, if the animal was only maintaining its weight the use of the term feed conversion would be nonsense. Thus feed conversion depends on the level of feeding. The higher the level of feeding the lower the proportion used to maintain the animal and the lower the feed conversion.

It is more meaningful to compare the food utilization of different feed items such as cereals, with similar types of animal. For instance the feed conversion of calves or lambs given oats, wheat, maize, barley or sorghum can help to evaluate which cereal is the most economical to feed.

Lactation

Consideration of energy required for milk production in cows is even more complicated than for growth. The cow almost invariably eats more feed, and there is yet another product so that there are three types of requirement: maintenance, milk and growth. The growth in turn can be positive (live weight gain) or negative (live weight loss). A further complication in late lactation is that there is generally a calf to support in the uterus. It is therefore no wonder that there are many values for energy requirements for milk production.

The requirements can only really be determined in respiration chambers in which the total heat produced is measured. In early lactation some fat is taken from the body and, as discussed earlier, this is a natural process which should not be discouraged. But in order to utilize the fat more dietary protein has to be given, as discussed elsewhere. Another complication is that live weight loss is not a clear indicator of energy loss.

Compared to other processes, such as increases in body energy, lactation is generally quite efficient. Since the composition of milk varies, particularly in the content of fat, the requirement for milk production is usually given as energy per unit of 4% fat-corrected milk. This is simply a means of changing milk to a standard fat content. If the fat content is greater than 4% then the yield of fat-corrected milk is higher than the actual yield, and *vice versa* for milk containing less than 4% fat.

In late lactation extra feed has to be given to meet the requirements of the unborn, and normally extra feed for storage as fat has also to be provided.

Energy values of feeds

Having ascertained the most important function for which the animal requires energy, let us now discuss the various methods and degrees of sophistication that are used in expressing the value of feeds.

Dry matter content

There is no disagreement in stating that water has no energy value; in fact a high water content can have a negative value insofar as the animal has to heat up the moisture in the feed to body temperature. Whether or not it has a negative value depends on whether the waste heat produced by the animal is exceeded by the heat necessary to bring the water in the feed to body temperature. The succulent feeds such as roots, fresh grass and silage, contain considerably more water than dry matter. Roots, for example, contain 80 to 90% water. The first approximation to feed value is therefore to determine dry matter content, which is usually determined by drying the feed at 100° for 24 to 48 hours.

Digestible dry matter

It can also be agreed that the part of the feed which is not utilized or digested by the animal has no value. In fact this too has a negative value. It costs some energy for the animal to propel indigestible components through the gut. We must therefore have an estimate of the digestibility of the dry matter of the feed. The standard method is to measure carefully in the live animal the dry matter consumed and the dry matter excreted. However, digestibility is often calculated from other measurements or determined as the so-called *in vitro* digestibility, which essentially is the digestion occurring in small artificial rumens in a laboratory.

Digestible organic matter

Digestible dry matter content corresponds quite closely to the energy value of a feed, but more accuracy can be achieved by determining the ash content of feeds. The organic matter content may then be calculated as the difference between the total dry matter and ash content, therefore the higher the ash content the lower the organic matter content. Ash consists of mineral material and has no energy value. Some feeds consistently contain more ash than others because of their natural composition and others may have high ash levels because they are contaminated with soil (which is mainly mineral material). Ash is determined as the residue from burning at high temperature (550°). The term digestible organic matter can be used when the ash in the feeds and in the dung has been determined.

Digestible energy

It is possible to estimate the digestible energy value by measuring directly the heat of combustion of the feed and of dung. This is particularly useful because different constituents of feed organic matter have different energy values. Thus the energy in one unit of fat is more than twice that of starch or cellulose.

Metabolizable energy (ME)

When the ruminant ferments feed some methane gas is formed in the stomach and this gas has no value as a nutrient. Metabolizable energy (ME) is a refinement of digestible energy and is calculated by subtracting the energy in the methane gas and the energy in the urine from the digestible energy. While the energy in the urine can be determined with simple tools the gas can only be determined in sophisticated respiration chambers. It is no surprise therefore that most of the ME values are derived by calculations from digestibility trials, using methane values determined on similar feeds. This method of feed evaluation is now used a great deal in several countries but it must be remembered that ME values determined by this method are no more precise than the original values from which they are calculated. It is often the case that scientists and commercial nutritionists calculate something which appears sophisticated from something rather simple.

Net energy

The net energy is, so to speak, the animal's assessment of ME. This is the value which the animal really needs to know, namely the extent to which ME is utilized in beef production, milk production or for maintaining the animal. It is therefore the value of the products of digestion and absorption. The net energy for lactation is the increase in energy in milk that the ME produces.

The net energy is a difficult determination to make insofar that it can only be determined by measuring heat exchange in sophisticated chambers similar to those used for methane production, or by carcase analysis. Therefore it is not possible to determine net energy for many feeds because of the expense. The starch equivalent system which was used for many years was based on net energy and many systems still are. The weakness is that animals use ME differently for different types of production so that the net energy value of a given food varies with the type of production.

In Scandinavia most feeds are given a value in feed units which is a very useful method for farmers to compare different feeds. A feed unit is the amount of feed which has the same net energy content of 1 kg barley. As mentioned earlier, the main reason why net energy is not used elsewhere is because it has different values for different types of production. Even so, having a standard of the feeding value of a common cereal is very useful.

Meeting requirements

Whatever method of feed evaluation is the preferred one the needs of the animal must be expressed in similar terms otherwise ration formulation becomes a very complicated affair. The requirements of the animals can be looked up in the tables produced by organizations such as the Ministry of Agriculture and the Agricultural and Food Research Council in the UK and by other organisations elsewhere.

On the face of it then it is an easy job for the farmer to look up the requirements and find the cheapest combination of feeds to feed to his animals, but every stockman will know that it is not so simple as that. While scientists are busy improving the precision of the operation there are many inaccuracies, some of which will be discussed briefly.

Inaccuracies

It has already been mentioned that as far as requirements for growth are concerned the composition of the live weight gain is crucial. This is not always easy to assess, even from tables giving composition of gain for different breeds at varying live weights because previous nutrition has a great effect. Every stockman knows that cattle given a low level of nutrition during winter will show compensation at grass, while cattle given a high level of nutrition during winter may lose weight on turnout during the compensating period to grass. This is because the composition of gain is to a large extent protein and water and is therefore very cheap from an energy point of view. By contrast the weight gain in adequately nourished animals consists mainly of fat. Therefore if during the winter cattle or sheep are given a relatively high level of feeding, or protein such as fishmeal which is not destroyed in the rumen, then there would be very little compensatory gain at grass. This only serves to illustrate that there is a great inaccuracy in estimating reliably requirements for growth, particularly if previous nutrition is unknown.

As far as lactation is concerned we are not much better off, except that it is relatively easy to measure the weight and composition of the main product, namely the milk. The inaccuracy is due to the fact that a lactating animal is almost always carrying out more than one activity; in early lactation it is losing fat, in mid-lactation it is gaining fat and in late lactation it is normally gaining fat and feeding the unborn calf. This again adds a source of inaccuracy.

Since the ME value of a feed is normally estimated from laboratory measurements there is a great deal of uncertainty as to its real feeding value, particularly in the case of roughages. The feeds with the least variation are probably cereals, roots and other concentrates. The feeds which vary most are roughages particularly silage and hay, where the stage of maturity and success of preservation are major factors. In addition, as the amount of feed increases so there is generally a reduction in digestibility. Such reductions can also be calculated from feed tables but unfortunately the extent of reduction in digestibility with increasing feeding level depends on the type of feed and on the amounts given, so the so-called level of feeding correction is not very accurate.

The most serious inaccuracies of feeding value will probably arise when feeds are mixed together. This has been discussed in Chapter 2 and is nearly always a reflection of reduced digestibility of the fibrous part of the feed when a higher proportion of concentrate is fed. Combining feeds can easily result in only half of the potential value of a hay, silage or straw being realized. It is no wonder that dairy cows in particular often give disappointing feed utilization. A great deal of the feeds may simply not be digested. Methods of partially avoiding these problems were also discussed in Chapter 2.

Due to the inaccuracies involved in estimating both requirement and feed value, there are many good reasons why stockmen should constantly observe how the animals perform. If performance is a great deal less than expected, there may be digestion problems such as those described earlier.

CHAPTER 5

PROTEIN REQUIREMENTS

The lean body mass of an animal – the muscles, organs, intestines – consist mainly of protein and water. Wool and hair likewise are almost pure protein. The animal itself cannot synthesize a number of the building blocks for protein, namely the so-called essential amino acids. Therefore, in order to increase the protein content of the body the animal needs a supply of protein.

The word animal is used deliberately here because the rumen microbes can use simple compounds such as ammonia and urea from which to make their cells. In fact they can use any compound which will decompose to ammonia – even urine. Microbial protein can then provide the animal with most of its protein needs. So in effect, it is not necessary to feed the ruminant animal any protein at all since the microbes in the rumen can make it for them.

Body fat, as will be discussed elsewhere, is essentially a spare resource of food which has been stored and can be used when the energy from the diet is not sufficient to meet the animal's needs. It cannot supply protein.

Methods of assessing requirements

It was, of course, most logical when the importance of protein was established, to determine the protein in the feed as the nitrogen (N) content x 6.25 because pure protein contains 16% nitrogen and 100/16 = 6.25. The animal's requirement was expressed as digestible protein or digestible crude protein (DCP) as it was obvious that only the digestible part of the protein could be used by the animal. Since there was little knowledge about the rumen microbes it was usual to subtract the N in the feed which was not really protein, non-protein nitrogen (NPN), from the total N and the remainder was called true protein.

When it was shown in the late 1940s that microbes could convert the NPN to protein for the animal, the system of DCP began to be inadequate. Added to this problem came the realization that almost all the protein in feeds was destroyed by the bacteria. A bigger problem arose when it was shown that nearly all protein in the dung consisted of indigestible microbial cells and only very little protein from the diet was true indigestible protein. This of course meant that the measured digestibility had very little meaning as far as actual digestibility of feed protein was concerned. Furthermore, if microbial growth occurred in the hind gut of the animal (see Chapter 2) then the microbes were not digested at all but passed out in the dung. This further complicated the expression of protein digestibility, as a small change in the amount of feed fermented in the large intestine could cause great changes in the measured protein digestibility.

The DCP system is being substituted by other systems based on more logical concepts, which have been published in detail by ARC (1984)*. Here the new approach and the logic behind it will be discussed.

The first principle to remember about new systems of protein evaluation is that they basically consider the microbes and their nutrition as separate from the animal itself and its protein supply. There are good reasons for this. First of all it is then possible to incorporate NPN logically into assessment of requirements. NPN can be used to meet microbial requirements. Failure to meet microbial requirements for N has repercussions on feed utilization, which can be avoided with cheap sources of N such as urea.

Secondly, when the animal itself requires more protein than that supplied by the microbial cells it is essential that some dietary protein escapes destruction by the rumen microbes, that is it is not degradable in the rumen. This type of protein is known as undegradable dietary protein (UDP), as distinct from rumen degradable protein (RDP). The microbes can only use RDP. The animal itself can use microbial protein formed from RDP and also dietary UDP.

It can now be seen that the term digestible crude protein is no longer useful. We need to know for feeds in general, and protein supplements in particular, the total crude protein content, how much is RDP and how much is UDP.

Microbial requirements

The microbes can, as mentioned before, use NPN and also RDP, which is broken down in the rumen to amino acids and ammonia. They can also use some area which is returned to the rumen from saliva and blood.

The amount of protein which microbes produce by increasing cell numbers and which subsequently becomes available to the animal is almost completely dependent on the amount of energy fermented. This has the important result that the production of microbial protein is related to the fermentability of the diet and, since the amount fermented is generally closely related to the digestibility of the feed, the microbial

---

*Agricultural Research Council (1984). *The Nutrient Requirements of Ruminant Livestock Supplement No. 1*, Commonwealth Agricultural Bureaux, Farnham Royal.

requirement is also related to digestibility. In more modern terms we convert digestibility to metabolizable energy (ME) and express the need of the microbes as RDP per megajoule (MJ) of ME. But it is important to understand why this is so.

The consequence is that the requirement for RDP is considerably less with straw than for concentrates because straw is less digestible. If more RDP is given than the microbes can utilize then it is simply wasted and excreted in the urine.

The crucial question then is what happens if the rumen microbes are getting less RDP than they require? There are occasions where, in fact, it would be tempting to feed less dietary protein because the protein needs of the animal are less than that which the microbes produce. Here the evidence is quite clear. In fact the necessity to feed adequate RDP is more to ensure efficient feed utilization than to meet the protein requirements of the animal. If the RDP supply is deficient the digestibility of the feed will be reduced and in consequence feed intake will be depressed. The ARC state the requirement of the microbes as 7.8 g crude protein as RDP per MJ of ME.

Animal requirements

Unlike microbes the requirements of the animal vary depending on the amount of protein produced in lean meat, milk or wool. The amount of lean body growth per day is almost the same in a calf as it is in a steer approaching slaughter weight, yet the steer will eat twice as much feed dry matter per day, so the total protein supply per unit of feed dry matter must be higher for the young animal. The cow in early lactation will yield more milk and eat less food than she does in mid-lactation. Consequently the need for protein per unit of feed is greater in early lactation because the cow has relatively little stored protein but generally a relatively large store of fat. Merino sheep will need more protein for wool growth than Suffolk sheep. If an animal is only maintaining itself at the same weight it needs only sufficient protein to maintain lean body mass.

Maintenance

It was mentioned before that if enough energy is given to maintain the animal then the microbial protein produced from RDP is likely to be sufficient to meet the maintenance requirement for protein. However, if the animal is fed less than its maintenance requirement for energy then microbial protein production is not enough and consequently it will lose not only body fat but also protein or lean tissue.

Growth

When a young ruminant is weaned before the time at which it would naturally be weaned if it were left sucking with its mother then the requirement for protein is greater than the supply from the microbes and UDP must be supplied in the feed. The animal left with its mother will of course get protein from milk in such a way that the rumen is by-passed via the oesophageal groove, as discussed earlier (Chapter 1). This is however a generalization and it is necessary to discuss a few more details.

On the whole the higher the growth rate, relative to the size of the animal and to the amount of feed the animal will eat, the higher is the protein concentration required in the feed. This means that there are differences in requirement between breeds of animals. Fast growing breeds have a higher requirement than slow growing breeds, e.g. Charolais versus Aberdeen-Angus, Suffolk versus Cheviot and so on. Entire males will grow faster than females and castrates and therefore have a higher requirement for protein. In other words, the live weight at which the RDP or rumen microbial protein is sufficient for the animal varies between breeds and sexes. On the whole the greater the mature weight of the animal the higher is the weight at which microbial protein becomes adequate.

Lactation

Cows, ewes and nanny goats will all give a great deal more milk than that which could result from the amount of feed they eat. This is because they have stored feed on their back in the form of fat. Attempts to feed sufficient concentrates to high yielding animals to avoid loss of fat usually present other problems.

It is, however, very important to remember that fat from the body gives rise to no microbial protein and an animal has very little stored protein. As a result the requirement for UDP is relatively large in early lactation and is proportional to the extent to which the animal is in 'negative energy balance' – that is, the extent to which it is underfed relative to milk production, or the extent to which body fat is used to produce milk.

Pregnancy

If an animal is sustaining pregnancy alone, as with sheep and beef cattle, then the dietary RDP is generally about adequate until a few weeks before lambing or calving. The extent to which UDP is then required obviously depends on the size of the calf or the number of lambs or kids. *The problem of protein supply is generally aggravated by the fact that the greater the weight of the foetus(es) the less the animal can eat because the volume of the stomach is becoming limited (Fig. 21).* Since the requirement for protein is increasing as feed intake decreases, then the need for a supply of UDP in late pregnancy can be readily understood.

FIGURE 21   **The greater the weight of the foetus, the less the animal can eat**

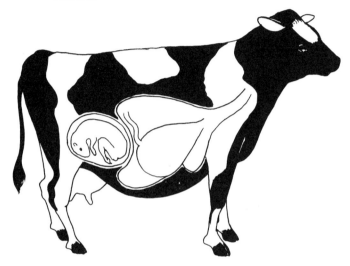

Consequences of protein deficiency

During growth

It is impossible to evaluate the problem of protein supply without knowledge of what happens if requirements are not met. For example if the animal is not receiving enough protein then lean tissue growth is reduced to that which is made possible. Since gain in weight in growing animals is mainly in the form of lean tissue it follows that the growth rate is reduced together with feed conversion efficiency, assuming that RDP requirements are met.

The question is whether a period of less than optimal growth can be compensated for later? If the animal is kept at maintenance or less in winter or during dry seasons, it will show compensatory growth whenever the deficiency is corrected. This is well known both in the tropics and sub-tropics in rainy seasons and in temperate regions when winter periods are followed by lush grass in the spring. As a result it may not always be economical to meet the optimal need for protein if the animal is to have a period of grazing prior to slaughter or if it is to be slaughtered during the rainy season. If the animal receives enough protein during the period of low level nutrition it will show much less compensatory growth. While it is always likely to be economical to feed adequate RDP it may not always be economical to feed enough UDP. Thus protein requirements relative to body weight differ according to previous protein nutrition. An undernourished animal has a higher need relative to its weight when nutrition is being restored than an animal which has been adequately fed all the time.

During lactation

Unlike growing animals, lactating females cannot usually show much compensatory milk production since the animal's body or lean mass can only buffer for small deficiencies in protein supply. As mentioned before the protein supply in early lactation is crucial to establish a high peak yield, which can influence the yield through the remainder of the lactation.

It is often considered that ewes are not like Friesian cows and therefore need not get the same attention. In fact, as mentioned in Chapter 1, relative to body weight a ewe feeding two or more lambs is yielding milk equivalent to a Friesian cow giving 30 to 35 kg a day, due to the fact that ewe's milk has a much higher fat content. Yet a ewe seldom gets the same attention in feeding. Protein for ewes in early lactation is as important as it is for high yielding cows.

During pregnancy

The foetus has a high priority and the animal will in fact use lean body mass to sustain foetal growth in periods of dietary deficiency. This has the effect of weakening the mother, making her more susceptible to problems such as prolapse and making it difficult to produce an udder ready for a high milk yield during lactation. In more severe cases the weight of the foetus will be reduced and its viability at birth will also be reduced. Combined with little or no milk in the udder this is indeed a bad start to life. It is no surprise therefore that animals have evolved to give birth to their young when feed supply is likely to be relatively good. In temperate regions this is late spring and early summer, and in arid regions when rain can be expected. Various mechanisms have evolved to ensure that this happens, such as mating during days of decreasing daylength in sheep.

Determining the protein value of feeds

The whole philosophy of RDP and UDP is relatively new and therefore much has still to be learned. The RDP and UDP in a feed are inter-related insofar that the crude protein is either RDP or UDP and the two make up

100% of the crude protein. The complication is that the difference between the two is not constant. The problem is greatest for small particles and therefore generally greater for protein supplements than for other feeds.

Let us imagine a cow consuming a mouthful of soyabean meal and let us follow what happens when that mouthful has been wetted by saliva and deposited in the fermentation chamber of the rumen. Since the particles of soyabean meal are small there are two options possible. It could either be degraded almost completely to RDP by the microbes, or it could pass out of the rumen undegraded because the particles are small enough to pass out. It is logical to assume that the speed at which the soyabean meal is degraded to RDP or passed out as UDP depends on the speed at which the two processes occur. The speed of degradation, the speed of outflow and thus the effective RDP/UDP ratio is not constant for one feed because the speed of outflow varies, in particular with level of feeding. It is therefore necessary to give different RDP/UDP values to the soyabean meal depending on feeding level and other circumstances. For instance, different values have been derived for dairy cows compared to growing cattle or suckler cows (Table 5.1).

TABLE 5.1 **Example of differences in the percentage of RDP and UDP in protein supplements for different feeding systems.**

Protein Source	Dairy Cows		Fattening Cattle		Suckler Cows	
	RDP	UDP	RDP	UDP	RDP	UDP
Soyabean	50	50	65	35	85	15
Fishmeal	30	70	35	65	40	60

The new protein system requires a different approach which farmers, feed compounders and animals will all benefit from in the future.

CHAPTER 6

PREPARATION AND PROCESSING OF FEEDS

Hay

The packaging of hay is very much governed by local technology and the cost of manual labour. The greatest labour requirement is needed when hay is handled in the loose form. In recent years square bales, small and large round bales, and large rectangular bales have emerged as labour saving devices. When the cost of energy was low there was a move towards artificially drying of hay. This is now too expensive, though drying by forced cold air ventilation in the barn is carried out in some areas.

Silage

The making of grass silage has increased greatly in popularity in temperate regions due to the fact that a more predictable feed quality can be obtained and it is easier to mechanize than hay-making. Also, weather conditions are not as critical as with hay. The preservation of silage is due to the acid conditions created by microbial breakdown of soluble sugars in the crop. In many respects the initial fermentation has similarities with rumen fermentation. Since the acid is not removed lactic acid bacteria tend to predominate because they can survive at the lowest pH and eventually the whole process ceases at a pH below 4.0. The initial acid conditions can be assisted by spraying acids onto the silage with the result that less of the carbohydrate and protein in the silage is broken down and in many cases this helps to ensure a high quality silage, with less ammonia produced and also less volatile acids formed.

Silage-making is assisted greatly by exclusion of air which is accomplished by pressing with tractors and covering the pit with plastic so that what is called anaerobic or oxygen-free conditions are created as quickly as possible. When the silage is high in dry matter exclusion of oxygen combined with acid conditions should ensure a well-preserved silage. The problem here is that when air is no longer excluded then organisms using oxygen can survive and less acid is formed initially. High dry matter silages will easily deteriorate if they are not used quickly after opening of the silo and exposure to air. If vermin, birds, children or wind create holes in the covering sheets the silage will be partly destroyed due to aerobic conditions creating overheating.

The silage can be packaged in different ways – long or chopped, in pits, clamps or plastic bags, depending mainly on the most practical method for the individual producer. Plastic bags are becoming increasingly popular due to their versatility, low capital cost, and the ability to seal the bag very soon after harvest, to speed up the removal of oxygen.

Roots

The method of storing and processing root crops for winter feeding depends on the likely severity of the winter, the type of animal, and the degree of mechanization available. Thus when turnips, for example, are given to sheep they are normally grazed in areas where the sheep are staying out of doors for the winter. The storage of roots also depends on climatic conditions and on the type of farm. The important point is that they should be protected from freezing. Apart from increasing losses, frozen roots can cause early loss of teeth in ewes. The nutritional aspects of roots and their similarity with concentrate as a feed are discussed elsewhere (Chapter 2).

Physical processing of roots depends on the animals to which they are given. It is often done to increase speed of eating rather than the total amount eaten. Chopping of roots is also necessary to ensure adequate consumption by broken-mouthed ewes.

Straw

The conditions mentioned for hay are on the whole applicable also for straw. It can be collected from the field in sheaves and threshed at the farm, or it can be packaged in the field. Alternatively, the whole cereal crop can be harvested by forage harvester and the straw separated from the grain at the farm.

Straw can be packaged in square, round or rectangular bales, or it can be harvested by forage harvester as for silage. The method, on the whole, depends more on the technology available on the farm and the ease of handling afterwards than on its nutritive value. Sheep will generally consume more straw if it is given in the chopped form rather than long, while physical form makes very little difference to its consumption by cattle. Untreated straw is not normally fed in large quantities to sheep but chopped straw treated with alkali may be of interest (see later). On the other hand, if sheep are allowed to select the best parts of the straw, such as the leaves, by offering 30 to 40% in excess of daily intake, the quality of the straw consumed may be equal to good quality hay.

Physical processing of roughages

Physical processing of roughages may be done both for nutritional and for practical reasons, and it is probably useful to keep this in mind in the following discussion.

One of the factors restricting the intake of fibrous roughages is the speed at which long particles are reduced by chewing and rumination, to particles small enough to pass out of the rumen (see Chapter 3). If the roughages are finely ground then this restriction is removed. However, in many cases the particles pass out before they are digested properly. Therefore grinding can have the effect of increasing the speed at which fibre is consumed and the total amount eaten, but digestibility is reduced and in general, with the high cost of processing, the procedure is not cost-effective.

Chopping of straw or hay, in addition to having the effect of increasing the speed at which they are eaten, generally results in the animals having less possibility of selecting the best quality material. Digestibility is therefore likely to be lower than that of long materials.

The main reason for most of the physical processing of fibrous roughages is practical convenience. Ground hay and straw is sometimes pelleted with molasses and incorporated into feed pellets or wafers. It is one way in which straw and hay can be transported at reasonable costs, but on the whole the nutritional benefits are too small for large scale processing of this kind. Rough grinding in bale grinders or tub grinders is also largely done for practical convenience of feeding. If the roughages are to be mixed and given as part of complete diets then rough grinding or chopping is required in order to make mixing possible.

Upgrading straw

Caustic soda

Interest in improving straw is nothing new. During the latter part of the last century German scientists worked on the problem and came up with complicated processes involving caustic soda, high pressure, high temperature and rinsing. These processes have been simplified to the extent that no pressure, no increase in temperature and no rinsing is now used. While the original processes were industrial ones, on-farm processes have now been developed.

The advantage of caustic soda as a method of treating straw is that treatment is rapid. The increase in digestibility occurs almost immediately. It is necessary though to wait a few days after treatment because the caustic soda has to be converted to sodium bicarbonate before it is safe to feed. The content of bicarbonate in the straw can be an advantage sometimes when it is given with high amounts of concentrate to dairy cows.

The disadvantages of caustic soda are that in order to treat the straw uniformly it is necessary to process it into smaller pieces. This in itself is costly. The consumption of water is increased when animals eat caustic soda-treated straw, so that the amount of urine excreted is also increased. This leads to a greater demand for bedding and more urine to dispose of. The sodium in the urine can, in the long run, cause problems of soil structure in heavy soils. If caustic soda treated straw is fed as a large proportion of the feed then it has to be remembered that it is a very protein deficient feed and if no RDP is added the treatment effect is very small. Providing supplementary protein adds a further cost to the treatment and the most appropriate method is another obstacle to overcome on farms.

FIGURE 22   **Injecting ammonia into a sealed stack of straw**

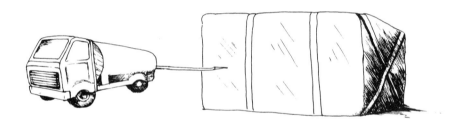

Ammonia

Ammonia is a volatile gas which can permeate through a stack of straw (Fig. 22). The effect on digestibility is similar to caustic soda but ammonia is a weaker alkali than caustic soda. As a result the reaction with the straw is much slower. In Britain, for instance, 2 to 4 weeks is required. The reaction can be speeded up by increasing the temperature and this has gained some practical application in the form of sealed boxes. The gas will seek the moisture in the straw and therefore some moisture in the straw is required. If the straw is very dry or about 10% moisture it may be necessary to add some moisture or to use the aqueous form of ammonia. If, on the other hand, the straw is too moist then uniform distribution of ammonia is difficult to achieve.

There are two large advantages of ammonia treatment over caustic soda treatment which make it more suitable as an on-farm treatment: (1) no physical processing is required, and (2) having increased the digestibility there is generally enough ammonia adhering to the straw to satisfy the additional requirement of the microbes so that no more RDP is required. It could also be stated that it is better to have an excess of urea in the urine, rather than sodium. In addition, the consumption of water is much less with ammonia than with caustic soda treated material. Many methods of ammonia treatment are available. These include stacks sealed with plastic sheeting, plastic bags for one or more bales, and purpose-built buildings for large-scale treatment. If the farmer is uncertain about his commitment to the treatment then he should try the plastic sheeting first, with no capital commitment.

There are essentially two forms of ammonia which can be used on farms – anhydrous ammonia, which must be kept under pressure, and aqueous ammonia, where the ammonia is dissolved in water and not kept under pressure. The two forms give about the same improvement in digestibility when the same amount of ammonia is applied per tonne of straw.

Urea

Urea can be used as a source of ammonia because it is converted to ammonia by an enzyme which is in the straw, at high moisture contents and at high ambient temperatures. Urea is therefore used in tropical areas as a source of ammonia for upgrading straws. In temperate regions it is generally too cold to count on complete breakdown of urea to serve as a source of ammonia, but as mentioned in Chapter 7 the urea is ideal for preservation and may be used both for its preservation properties and its nutritive properties. Also, the small amount of ammonia released will generally cause a small increase in digestibility. Urine can also be used since it contains urea, and this may be of some interest in poorer areas of the world.

Effects of upgrading on nutritive value

It has been mentioned before that a problem with untreated straw is the long time required for digestion due to the slow rate of fermentation, the low digestibility and the long time taken to reduce the particles to be small enough to pass out of the rumen. The main effects of alkali, be it ammonia or caustic soda, are to increase the proportion of the feed which is digested – usually by 10 to 15% and to speed up the time it takes to ferment, both of which will increase the capacity of the stomach to deal with more material per unit of time. As a result the animal eats more treated than untreated straw. Often a 10% increase in digestibility leads to a 50% increase in feed consumption and since the feed consumed is more digestible it leads to an even greater increase in consumption of metabolisable energy. Ruminants which would lose weight on untreated straw, even if urea was added at feeding time, will generally maintain themselves and even grow a little if they are fed on alkali-treated straw alone. It is important to remember that the evaluation of straw treatment should not merely be in terms of the 10 to 15% improvement in D value but should also take into account the increased amount of straw that can be fed in this way. On the other hand, if the animal receives a restricted quantity of straw then evaluation in terms of digestibility alone may be more relevant.

It is very important to appreciate the principle that if straw is improved in digestibility then there is an increase in the N needed for the bacteria to ferment it. Many feeding trials with caustic soda treated straw have given very poor results because this principle was not recognised. Instead of adding urea it is of course possible to feed the straw, particularly caustic soda treated straw, together with another material which has an excess of N, for instance excreta such as poultry manure. It is also possible to treat poultry manure with caustic soda so that the fibre in the manure is better digested, which in turn will make better use of the excess crude protein in this material.

Cereals

When cereal grains were first given to ruminants they were normally ground and boiled, since it was generally believed that the more thorough the pre-processing the more efficient digestion would be. Another reason for extensive processing was to ensure that hard seeds from weeds were completely destroyed otherwise they were likely to pass through the gut of the animal and, through the dung, on to the land. This latter reason is no longer relevant since modern combine harvesters can effectively clean out the weed seeds and furthermore herbicides ensure that only a few weeds have the possibility of contaminating cereals with seeds.

In recent years it has been recognised that little processing is required to ensure a high digestibility. *Over-processed cereals ferment too quickly which can give problems of acidosis, particularly in cattle fed on cereal-based diets and also in dairy cows given a cereal-based concentrate twice daily (Fig. 23).* Farmers have no doubt contributed to the general over-processing of cereals insofar that they normally assume that if some recognizable whole grains appear in the dung then they have all passed through! *The passage of the occasional whole grain has no measurable effect on digestibility, and the digestibility of roughage is reduced when grain is overprocessed (Fig. 24).* In fact no sign of any grain in the dung is likely to indicate that over-processing of grain has occurred.

FIGURE 23   **For cattle, grain needs to be crushed as in the left of the picture. Overprocessing, as in the right of the picture, is unnecessary and dangerous to health** *Photo: Rowett Research Institute.*

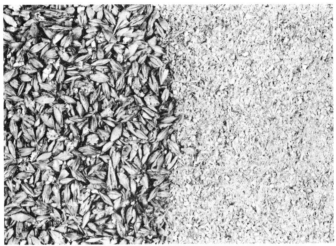

FIGURE 24   *The passage of a few whole grains in dung has little effect on digestibility. But digestibility of roughage is reduced by overprocessing of cereals*

The need for processing depends very much on the size of the animal. This is due partly to the fact that it is difficult for whole grain to pass through the opening from the rumen in small animals but quite easy in large animals. This means that grains which were not cracked during eating will be retained and cracked during rumination. As a result processing of cereals is not required for sheep, goats and even calves up to 100 to 150 kg live weight. In fact it is much healthier for the animal to eat whole grain both in complete cereal-based diets and as a supplement to roughages. When whole grain is fed to lambs, for instance, the physical structure of whole grain acts as a roughage so that it is not necessary to feed any roughage at all.

For larger cattle some processing is required since the animals do not crack all the grain in the first chewing and, since the opening allows passage of whole grain, there is a possibility that an unacceptable number of whole grains will pass out of the rumen and into the dung. Once a whole grain has slipped out of the rumen there is little likelihood of subsequent digestion. But it must never be thought that all the grains will pass out. It is very unlikely that the digestibility of whole grain given to cattle is less than 60%. Even so, processing is desirable for cattle but the principle must be that processing must be as gentle as possible. A scratch in the seed coat of the grain is almost sufficient so that bacteria can enter into the grain.

Several processes have developed which are suitable for light processing. They include rolling, crimping and treatment with caustic soda.

The problem with rolling is that in order to crush the smallest grains, the large grains are over-processed. It is desirable therefore that the smallest grains are not processed so as to ensure the optimum amount of crushing for the rest. Crimping relies on breaking the grains and is slightly better than rolling, since there is no problem of the size of grain.

CHAPTER 7

PRESERVATION OF FEEDS

Interest in the preservation of feeds is not new; it has been necessary ever since farmers, in areas of seasonal plant growth, ceased to be nomadic and decided on permanent settlements. It then became important to preserve feeds grown during the growing season for subsequent use during winter or drought periods. Also, because staple feeds such as grain only ripened once a year, preservation was required to ensure that man and animal could be nourished throughout the year.

The principle of preservation is to prevent bacteria and fungi from consuming the feed. The object therefore is to inhibit the growth and proliferation of spoilage organisms or at least to make life very uncomfortable for them so that losses through microbial action are minimal.

The optimal conditions for most organisms are: (a) temperatures between 10 and 40°C, (b) high moisture contents and (c) pH values between 5 and 8. In addition, most organisms thrive best when oxygen is present. Having stated the optimal conditions the most appropriate means of making conditions less than optimal should be considered. First of all it is possible to preserve by cooling the materials. This method is not generally used for agricultural products or animal feeds but may well be used in the future. Preservation can also be achieved by maintaining a high temperature, but this is normally too expensive. The method most used in the past was to remove sufficient moisture to ensure that microbial growth was very slow. Moisture contents of 16% or less are generally considered safe for preservation.

It is possible to remove oxygen, thus making conditions anaerobic. Alternatively it is possible to create alkalinity or acidity so that little microbial activity takes place. Initially it is also possible to use microbial poisons which are harmless to animals.

Grain

Drying

Harvesting, until the advent of the combine harvester, was almost exclusively based on drying the grain while it was still attached to the straw. Sheaves were stacked first in the fields and then in stacks before the grain was threshed out. While some grain harvested by combine harvester is sufficiently dry so that only a minimum of microbial activity takes place during storage, a great deal of it is not sufficiently dry for safe storage and must be dried or preserved.

For many purposes drying is the preferred method of preserving grain, i.e. for milling, brewing, distilling, seeds etc. The moisture content is usually reduced to 14-15%. There are many methods of drying which will not be described in detail here. Drying is the preferred method for grain which will enter the human food chain, as it is easier to transport and the moisture content is more uniform than with grain preserved by other methods.

Sealing

For grain which is to be used on the farm for animal feed and which can be incorporated rapidly into feeds after it has come out of storage, the method of anaerobic preservation is quite attractive. But the construction of sealed silos requires capital and it must therefore be the preservation method which is expected to be used for several years.

The problem with this method is the tendency for the grain to deteriorate quickly after it has been taken out of the silo. However, if urea is to be incorporated into the feed, it may be sprayed onto the grain as it is taken out of the silo to reduce problems of rapid aerobic deterioration. Preservation in large plastic bags, like silage, may also be of interest.

Cooling

As mentioned earlier, preservation by cooling is also possible and, since grain is a well insulated material, preservation by cooling may be less expensive than preservation by other methods when a suitable technology has been developed.

Acid treatment

The most commonly used acid is propionic acid which, apart from its acidic property, is more poisonous to spoilage organisms than most other acids at the same level of addition. The greater the moisture content the greater the amount of acid is required. If heat is evolved, condensation of water can be a problem on the surface of the grain stack. *The condensation of water will reduce acidity and so microorganisms may invade from the surface and a gradual deterioration can take place. This can be avoided, in part at least, by placing straw bales on top of the grain which will buffer the interface with cooler air (Fig. 25)* so that condensation takes place in the straw bales rather than on the grain itself. The bales can then be removed when there is no more heating in the stack. Propionic acid is normally sprayed on the grain as it is augered into the store.

FIGURE 25   **Straw bales placed on top of moist grain treated with
propionic acid can prevent deterioration of the grain at
the surface**

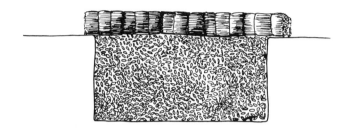

Alkali treatment

Grain may also be preserved by alkali. Treatment with caustic soda, for
example, not only preserves the grain, but no further processing is
required before it is given to cattle. However, the method has the
disadvantage that the grain will stick together into hard clumps and will
not flow into augers. These hard clumps can be broken up by spraying
water on the grain before feeding. If possible this should be carried out
several days before feeding, since the swelling of the treated grain when
exposed to water will assist its digestion by cattle.

Caustic soda can be sprayed on the grain as it passes through augers or
in feed mixer wagons. Some heating after treatment is likely and, as a
result, condensation of water may occur on the surface of the grain
heap. The moist grain on the surface will dissolve carbon dioxide from
the air and the pH will decrease towards neutrality. Thus the grain may
begin to deteriorate from the surface. The same principle as mentioned
before, with straw bales providing the interface with cold air, can be
used. The technique is still in the development stage and may prove too
difficult as caustic soda is a dangerous liquid to handle on farms.

Alternatively, ammonia may be used. It has the advantage that, apart
from creating alkaline conditions, free ammonia also has bacteriocidal
properties. The method has the additional advantage that if the grain is
subsequently used for feeding of ruminants, then the ammonia which
becomes attached to the grain can be used as a source of non-protein N
for the bacteria in the rumen.

But ammonia has the disadvantage that its use requires a reasonably
airtight grain silo. In addition, the accumulation of ammonia gas in silos
can be dangerous. As opposed to caustic soda, ammonia treatment does
not process the grain.

Recently it has been shown that urea can preserve high moisture grain. A solution of urea in water can be sprayed on the grain. The small release of ammonia from the urea serves to keep microorganisms to acceptably low levels. In fact, urea is generally cheaper than acid treatment and it has the advantage that when the grain is given to ruminants, the urea also serves as a source of non-protein N for the rumen microbes.

Urea can be sprayed on to grain as it passes through augers in the same way as, for instance, propionic acid. The amount of urea necessary to preserve the grain is between 1-2%, depending on the moisture content in the grain.

As with the other alkali treatment processes, the use of both ammonia and urea needs to be further explored on farms.

Microbial poisons

Compounds containing formaldehyde are also being explored for grain preservation. Some of these compounds could possibly have the effect of protecting the protein in the grain from being destroyed in the rumen.

Forages

Drying

As for grain, the traditional method of forage preservation was by drying, i.e. hay-making. This is still an excellent method in areas where the weather is reasonably predictable so that the drying process can be completed rapidly on a field scale. In many northern European countries hay-making is decreasing due to the uncertainty of making good hay to ensure a high and predictable level of productivity in the winter period. The soluble sugars in grass will, to a large extent, be washed out in heavy showers of rain, with a resultant loss of a very important part, and certainly the most digestible fraction, of the hay.

Artificial drying of hay is being undertaken, but the high cost of fuel and of capital equipment is making this conservation method for ruminant feeds too expensive. Barn drying is a much less energy-consuming method as cold air is circulated through hay baled at about 50 to 60% moisture.

Sealing

As for grain, it is also possible to preserve forage by exclusion of air. This method is being increasingly used for making haylage and for wilted and unwilted silage. It is very important that silos or plastic bags are sealed completely. If not, oxygen will enter and eventually moulds and bacteria will destroy the forage.

Preservation of forage by exclusion of air is relatively easy when care is taken in making airtight stacks or large bales. It is more difficult when the stacks have to be opened as aerobic deterioration can be rapid during the feed-out period. This is particularly important when large stacks are opened. The surface area exposed to air must be as small as possible to avoid extensive deterioration and the exposed face may need to be covered each time silage is removed.

Acid treatment

The art of making silage is essentially to create conditions where bacteria produce acid very quickly so that they eventually pickle themselves and all other organisms. The production of fermentation acids can be assisted by addition of organic acids such as formic and acetic acid, and inorganic acids such as sulphuric acid or by inoculation with the correct type of bacteria. This encourages the growth of the more desirable lactic acid bacteria. It is thus a method of preventing too many fermentation products from being formed, and of reducing the amount of protein being degraded to ammonia and other non-protein compounds.

Alkali treatment

Forage may be preserved by alkali treatment. Usually this method is of the greatest interest with low dry matter hay or perhaps haylage, straw, whole crop maize or barley. Preservation with alkali is normally only of interest if there is the additional bonus of increasing digestibility. This has been shown to occur when moist hay or whole-crop cereals are preserved with ammonia or urea. The alkali treatment of fibrous forages is discussed in more detail in Chapter 6.

CHAPTER 8

SHEEP NUTRITION

There are so many different sheep production systems that it is extremely difficult to make general comments, but an attempt will be made to divide the different systems into categories. It is probably most useful to discuss lamb nutrition separately from that of the ewe, recognizing that it cannot really be separated as the feeding of the ewe is affected by the number and desired nutrition of the lambs.

Artificial rearing of lambs

Artificial rearing of lambs is normally only practised for orphan lambs or when the number of lambs born to the ewe exceeds her capacity to rear them. If the milk from the ewe is to be sold for processing then of course there are very strong economic reasons for artificial rearing.

The general principle of artificial rearing has been discussed earlier (Chapter 1). Lambs can be trained to drink from a teat or from a trough. The earlier the lambs are weaned the easier it is to imprint a new feeding method on them. It is essential, however, that colostrum is given either from the ewe or via a stomach tube. Even cow's colostrum may have to be used. If the ewe has died during or after lambing then the lamb may be given the opportunity, if it is practical, to suckle another newly-lambed ewe to ensure that colostrum is received. The quantity required is about 50 ml/kg weight, or 200-300 ml per lamb.

Milk substitutes for lambs are generally higher in fat than those for calves. Ewes' milk generally contains 7 to 8% fat. They should also be more concentrated, i.e. contain less water than those recommended for calves. About 20% milk substitute dry matter and 80% water is about right. The milk substitute can be given *ad libitum* from an automated dispenser which also heats the water. Or it may be given as cold milk, which prevents the lamb from drinking too much at any one time. The best system, but also the most labour consuming, is no doubt hand feeding from a bottle, as this enables the stockman to see that all is well and that all the lambs are drinking. During the first week or so it is advisable to feed them three times per day. For very small lambs, this practice should continue for longer than a week. Thereafter the number of feeds may be reduced to twice daily.

From two weeks onwards a dry creep feed should be available to encourage solid feed consumption, so that the rumen can develop rapidly, and to enable the lamb to survive on solid food alone. The creep feed can consist of the fattening diet, but some stockmen find it useful to add to the diet palatable extras like flaked maize or grass cubes in small quantities. *It is very important that the feed trough is constructed so that the lambs cannot get their feet into the creep feed or soil it by other methods (Fig. 26).* Not only will this reduce intake drastically, it will also assist in spreading disease.

FIGURE 26   **Early weaned lambs eating from a hopper designed to prevent contamination by faeces** *Photo: Rowett Research Institute.*

Rearing early weaned lambs

As discussed in Chapter 1, lambs can be weaned at about 4 to 5 weeks of age and given solid food alone, provided that they have had access to a palatable creep feed before weaning. The best criteria for successful weaning is the amount of solid food consumed before weaning, which should be around 200 g/d. For lambs this measurement is seldom possible to obtain in practice, and age is the next best criteria. No lamb should be weaned at less than 4 weeks of age.

Since the rearing of early weaned lambs is very easy it has a great deal of relevance for several sheep production systems. In addition the cost of milk substitute is generally much higher than that of solid feed, so it is desirable to wean lambs onto solid food as soon as possible. Having accustomed them to solid feed, which for lambs will consist mainly of grain, there is generally little point in letting the animal out to grass at a later stage or introducing roughage, since lambs accustomed to grain feeding grow very fast and will achieve slaughter weight 2 or 3 months after weaning. Early-weaned lambs will normally not survive on grass alone, so a period of concentrate feeding is required. Generally it is most economical to complete the rearing on concentrate, if of course the lambs are to be sold as fat lambs.

In frequent breeding systems early weaning is required to combat lactation anoestrus, poor nutritional status or poor body condition of the ewes at mating. The correct condition of the ewe at mating is important to achieve high conception rates. There is, however, little point in weaning lambs at birth for early rebreeding since conception is difficult to achieve, in any case, before 4 to 6 weeks after lambing.

In hill and upland areas where the nutrition of the ewes is inadequate there may be a case for weaning one of each pair of twins at about 4 weeks of age and to leave the other lamb with the ewe. This would enable hill farmers deliberately to encourage higher productivity of the ewes and yet ensure the same proportion of fat lambs from the flock.

As with early weaning of twins in hill areas, it may also be worthwhile to wean one lamb out of each set of triplets in lowland flocks.

With lambs born out of season, for example in early winter when the ewes are fed indoors, it may be cheaper and easier to wean and rear them separately. The ewes may be given relatively cheap roughage diets until the spring, and the lambs could be reared rapidly on cereal-based diets.

The simplest form for lamb fattening is to draw the lambs from the ewes ready for slaughter, but most lambs from upland and hill areas end up as store lambs. There are many options of fattening the lambs. It must be remembered that these lambs have a mature stomach development enabling them to grow on roughage based diets alone.

The fattening of early weaned lambs is a relatively simple system though to be successful there are certain management factors which can be crucial for success.

FIGURE 27   **Early weaned lambs fattened on whole barley** *Photo: Rowett Research Institute.*

The diet developed at the Rowett Institute for rearing early weaned lambs consists of whole barley, wheat or maize, and high protein pellets consisting of 80% fish meal and 20% minerals, trace minerals and vitamins (Fig. 27). It is useful in this context if the same diet is also given to the ewes. This will familiarise the lambs with the feed and encourage high feed intakes as early as possible. For ewes, the proportion of high protein pellets in the diet should be about 10% and the pellet size similar to the size of grains to ensure uniform mixing.

The most important economic problem in indoor rearing systems is generally coccidiosis, which needs to be controlled. Dry bedding or wire floors for the lambs can assist in limiting the spread of these organisms.

Urinary calculi are generally related to magnesium intake. Often the magnesium content of diets for ewes can be such that it is dangerous for small lambs. Another problem sometimes encountered is muscular dystrophy or vitamin E/selenium deficiency. In some areas this needs to be prevented by injecting the lactating ewes with a vitamin E/selenium supplement.

A feed conversion of 3 kg feed per kg live weight gain can easily be obtained for early weaned lambs during their rearing period.

Early lamb production

For early finished lamb production from grass aftermaths, crop residues, roots or kale, no concentrate supplements are required. The problem here is that the lambs are often let on to stubbles or roots without sufficient adaptation. It is possible that grain has been spilt from the combine harvester, or that an area of cereals may have been left unharvested, for example due to damage resulting from heavy rain. Whatever the reason, cereals or high energy feeds are suddenly available *ad libitum*. This can be dangerous and result in many fatalities even although the grain is whole. It is advisable to let the lambs have access to such areas initially for a limited time each day.

If early lambs are to be supplemented, then whole grain is probably the cheapest feed and can, in many instances, be offered directly on the ground in dry areas with relatively little wastage. Use of light grain or seconds is often economical for this purpose. Generally the forage on offer at the same time will supply sufficient protein for the animal.

Late lamb production

Here there is a host of different systems and it is only possible to discuss generalizations. Late lambs are generally marketed when they are 9 to 12 months old in order to achieve the relatively high prices for lamb normally expected early in the year, from January to April, in the UK. This usually means that the lambs will experience a store feeding period or a period of relatively low-level nutrition. This is often achieved by offering no supplements in periods when grass is low in quantity and quality. As distinct from early lambs they require supplementary feed throughout the finished period, though in some area turnips may be available for grazing as the sole feed.

Lambs which have experienced store feeding or a period of low-level nutrition have an increased requirement for protein and will respond to small quantities of protected protein such as fish meal by increasing live weight gain. This can be given in a highly concentrated form, as a supplement to high quality roughage.

There are probably few supplements which are easier and cheaper than whole loose grains of barley, oats, maize or even wheat. Second quality grain is quite acceptable. The feeding of whole grain and its effect on roughage digestion and utilization has been discussed elsewhere (Chapter 6). If it is economic the supplement can also be distillery grains or sugar beet pulp. As discussed above, a high protein concentrate should be mixed with these feeds.

Intensive lamb production

Here the ewe which is lambing more than once per year must be considered. Lambing three times in two years is most common. The ewe's nutrition has to be well managed in order to achieve a healthy system of production, with a high number of lambs per pregnancy. During mating, whether handmating or artificial insemination, the ewe must be in good or in rising condition. While this is generally agreed as a desirable objective, it is not always so easy to achieve in practice.

If the ewe is lambing every 8 months she has only 3 months between lambing and mating. Some ewes, due to repeat inseminations and the initial spread of lambing, will have less than 2 months. As a result early weaning of the lambs is necessary even if the ewe is milking heavily. In any case the ewe will often not conceive when she is being suckled. Reducing food intake to decrease milk yield can have the effect that the ewe will milk even more from body fat and then be in poorer condition for mating. It is probably simpler to reduce the protein in the feed which can often reduce milk yield, even if the ewe is consuming large quantities of feed.

A month or so after mating it is advisable to feed the ewe only a maintenance diet, which can be achieved by a high stocking rate at grass or feeding a fibrous diet. Hay, ammonia treated straw or silage may constitute the sole feed if the ewes are kept indoors. *Alternatively, untreated high quality straw may be used if the ewes are allowed to refuse about 25%. They will then select the leafy portions (Fig. 28).* A few weeks before lambing, depending on the availability and quality of roughage, the ewe may have to be supplemented with concentrates. The inclusion of high-protein supplements a couple of weeks before lambing and 3 to 4 weeks after lambing will help to ensure adequate udder development and high milk yield in early lactation, particularly if the protein is protected from degradation in the rumen. For out of season lambing nutrition is often excessive. For example ewes are often overfat when lambing in late summer and are consequently prone to twin lamb-disease (pregnancy toxaemia) or acetonaemia. As for so many mammals, including humans, over-feeding is almost as undesirable as underfeeding.

FIGURE 28   Sheep select the leafy portion of straw and leave the stemmy parts uneaten. On the left of the picture is the straw at the start and on the right the stemmy material remaining after one hour. *Photo: Rowett Research Institute.*

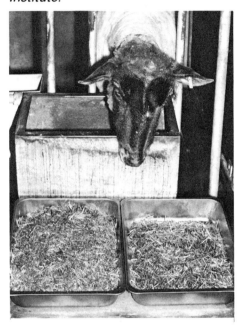

Lowland ewes

For lowland ewe flocks it is convenient to discuss flocks lambing early, in January and February, and later lambing flocks, since the problems of nutrition are slightly different.

Early lambing ewes have normally been grazing on stubble or pasture until close to lambing and they then have to be supplemented with concentrate feeds both during the latter part of pregnancy and during most of their lactation to ensure high milk yield, rapid lamb growth and early finishing of lambs when prices are high in late spring and early summer.

The feeding of the early lambing ewe has a great deal in common with that of the dairy cow. There is a temptation to feed excessive amounts of easily digestible carbohydrate such as pelleted concentrate, and since the consumption of roughage (hay, silage, ammonia treated straw etc.) is generally not measured, the amount of concentrate given is often so high that the consumption and indeed the digestibility of the roughage is very much reduced and the ewe is on the verge of acidosis. The ewe stops eating, which in turn causes twin lamb disease in pregnancy and ketosis or acetonaemia in lactation. The ewe is best fed with very high quality roughage and only a little concentrate.

The composition of the concentrate is as important here as it is for dairy cows. *Sugar beet pulp is a better supplement than pelleted grain supplements; whole grain is superior to pelleted concentrate. Protein supplements can be mixed with whole grain or dry pellets of sugar beet pulp (Fig. 29).* Here again, protected proteins or fish meal are preferable. The quantity of supplement depends entirely on the quality of the roughage.

New technologies of scanning ewes to diagnose pregnancy and to determine which ewes are carrying more than one lamb have made strategic feeding much easier. Ewes can be grouped according to stage of pregnancy and number of foetuses. It should be pointed out though that ewes in poor condition, even if they are carrying single lambs, might well be grouped with those carrying two or more. Scanning does not remove the judgment of the stockman as to the most appropriate level of nutrition for the individual animal.

Later lambing lowland ewes require free access to good quality roughage — hay, silage or root crops are generally adequate during pregnancy as the ewes will normally be lambing when the grass is growing. Barley straw can also be very useful provided refusals of about 25% are allowed. This means that the ewes can select the most nutritious leafy part of the straw and leave the most indigestible rough stemmed parts. If the straw is ammonia-treated a lower level of refusal is required. Supplements of concentrate may be required only for a couple of weeks before lambing, depending on the quality of the roughage on offer during pregnancy. The nutrient which is generally deficient is protein. Small amounts of a supplement high in protected protein, such as fishmeal or meat and bone meal, are more appropriate than larger quantities of a lower protein material. The protein supplement will help to ensure adequate udder development and an efficient use of body fat until grass is available in sufficient quantity to sustain lactation and growth rate of the lambs.

Hill ewes

The problem with hill ewes is one of supplementing poor quality roughage with RDP so as to maximize intake and digestion of the available roughage. It is also necessary to supply small amounts of energy to prevent excessive loss of weight and to ensure healthy lambs.

In severe under-nutrition both the weight and viability of the offspring can be adversely affected.

Supplementation with a source of RDP such as urea presents some difficulties insofar as urea cannot be provided on its own and should ideally be given several times per day. Ideally the supplements should contain small amounts of energy and a relatively large amount of RDP. It is, for instance, possible to provide blocks containing urea, minerals and molasses or whole grains.

Protein supplementation at or around lambing time improves udder development and initial milk yields. Vegetable or animal protein supplements may also be incorporated into feed blocks and licks.

FIGURE 29   **Supplements such as sugar beet pulp and high-protein feeds can be mixed with whole grains for sheep** *Photo: Rowett Research Institute.*

CHAPTER 9

BEEF CATTLE NUTRITION

In discussing energy requirements for growth (Chapter 4) it was emphasised that whenever the term requirement is used the next question must be requirement for what? In the beef animal, growth rate can vary from the absolute growth potential of between one and two kg/d depending on genotype, to only a small proportion of the growth potential, or possibly a certain amount of live weight loss.

The level of beef cattle nutrition required is very much a question of economics which can vary from year to year, and certainly from country to country as the economics of beef production may be stimulated or discouraged by political decisions. It is, of course,also determined by region and climate.

This enormous variation in economic and environmental circumstances has the effect that the age of slaughter of otherwise similar genotypes may well vary from about 1 year in intensive systems to as much as 4 years in very extensive systems. It is therefore not possible to provide a blueprint for the feeding of beef cattle as this may vary enormously and is further complicated by the fact that what is regarded in one area as a desirable carcass composition may not meet the criteria in another area or in another country. On the other hand, there is no doubt that in most situations there is a desire to produce less fat and more protein.

This desire for less fat and more lean meat in the carcass brings about changes in breeding policies. Thus the slaughter of animals is occurring more frequently at an earlier stage of their mature liveweight. In order to retain the same weight at slaughter this means that a higher mature weight of the breeding stock is required. In most breeds this is indeed the trend. It is also more economical for the terminal sire to be of a larger breed rather than the dam, in order to avoid the higher maintenance costs of a very large female – hence the increase observed over the last few years in the use of large breeds such as the Charolais and the Simmental as terminal sires.

Intensive beef production

This system is almost invariably based on indoor production. In most instances the animals are early-weaned calves from dairy farms. In the section on early weaning to solid feed (Chapter 1) some aspects relating to this system have already been discussed.

In order to maintain a high growth rate to ensure that the calves reach slaughter weight during the desired period, there must be no energy or protein deficiency to restrict the realization of maximum growth potential. This almost invariably means feeding on cereals, cereal by-products or highly soluble carbohydrate by-products.

The rapid turnover of cereals in the rumen and the high nutrient density of digestible feeds enable calves to consume large quantities. It is almost essential that such diets are available *ad libitum*. If the feed troughs are empty for any length of time, or dirty, then there is the possibility of overeating and acidosis when new feed is introduced.

The feeding of cereals or soluble carbohydrates such as molasses means that any cellulosic or fibrous feeds such as hay have virtually no nutritional value. Fibre digestion is negligible. However, *ad libitum* access to straw has the effect of adding some fibrous structure to the diet so that many health problems can be avoided. The roughage, while of little or no value nutritionally, helps to abrade dead cells from the wall of the stomach so that the acids are absorbed quickly. It also stimulates a greater production of saliva, which helps to prevent too much acidity in the rumen.

Roughage also reduces somewhat the habit of licking and swallowing of hair. If the rumen wall is inflamed cattle hairs can become embedded in the wall and eventually penetrate, allowing bacteria to invade the liver. For many years most livers from calves fattened intensively were discarded due to liver abscesses (see Chapter 2).

It is very important that the cereals used in intensive beef production are not overprocessed. In fact, for some cereals like maize, when given as the sole feed, no processing is preferable; for oats it is also questionable whether processing helps feed utilization. From a health point of view the absolute minimum processing which allows a reasonable digestibility is the optimum strategy. Unlike lambs and goats, cattle above about 150 to 200 kg live weight require some processing of barley and wheat otherwise too many whole grains will pass into the dung. This aspect has been discussed earlier(Chapter 6).

Protein supplements should be used but it is quite probable that the best combination is to spray urea on the grain, which can also be used to preserve the grain. It is then possible to use a relatively small quantity of a protected or partially protected protein supplement, such as fishmeal or blood meal. This can be mixed with grain on the farm.

Because of the amount of heat produced by intensively fed cattle it is very important that the houses are well ventilated, otherwise respiratory diseases will claim a great toll and most of the profit.

Many beef cattle reach slaughter weight at around 18 months of age in temperate regions where good grassland is available. This, of course, means that regardless of whether the calves are spring or autumn born they will almost invariably spend one winter indoors. Depending on their age some cattle will be fattened at grass and some during the second winter.

It is beyond the scope of this book to enter into aspects of grassland management, however important, but the winter feeding period will be discussed in some detail.

Depending on the age of the animals at housing, there may be some doubts about whether all will reach slaughter weight before the spring. In fact some farmers feed a high quality diet to all cattle and expect some to finish during the winter while others will be let out for a short grazing period. This practice is generally inefficient for the later-finishing animals due to the fact that cattle which have been fed on a high quality diet during the winter show little, if any, compensatory growth during the early grazing period. In fact some may even lose weight during the first 2 to 3 weeks at grass. The other, and possibly more important aspect related to overall feed utilization, is that the utilization of fibrous roughages will almost invariably be depressed with high level feeding of supplementary concentrate during the winter period. From the point of view of feed utilization it is more appropriate to feed animals that are to be fattened on grass on a high cellulose diet such as hay, straw or silage and obtain compensatory growth at grass. If the animals are to be finished indoors during the winter less emphasis needs to be given to cellulose digestion. In fact, the cattle may well be finished quickly on a high concentrate diet so that fibrous roughage is given more to provide a structure in the feed and ensure healthy animals than to provide nutrients.

Store cattle

Feeding for over-wintering is aimed primarily at low cost feeds. The nature of the low cost feeds vary from one area to another. In addition to hay, silage and straw other relatively cheap by-products may be available such as tops or stalks from various cash crops. The amount of digestible feed the animals can consume varies both between and within the materials mentioned. As discussed in the chapter on feed intake (Chapter 3), it is at present not very easy to predetermine from any chemical measurement of the feed exactly how much the cattle will eat except that, all other things being equal, the better the quality the more they will eat.

It may be useful for the livestock producer to decide the rate of gain that he wishes to achieve during the store period and to weigh the animals monthly. For instance, if a rate of gain of 500 g/d is required he may have the following options:

1   *Ad libitum* silage

2   *Ad libitum* hay

3   *Ad libitum* untreated straw + 2 kg cereal grain

4   *Ad libitum* ammonia treated straw + 300 g fish meal

If the required gain is not achieved after a period of 6 weeks or so then it may be necessary to give the animals a concentrated feed such as sugar beet pulp or cereals. The options given above are only a guide, because of the difficulty of assessing the intake of fibrous roughages. Obviously the animals must also have access to the required minerals, particularly when straw diets are used.

The same feeds can be used for finishing store cattle as mentioned earlier for the intensive beef system. But since the animals are used to consuming roughages, care must be taken when introducing cereals in large quantities. A gradual change must be made, starting perhaps with 500 g/d and increasing daily by about 250 g/d until the required level of supplementation is reached or until a complete cereal diet is achieved.

It must again be emphasised that as soon as the level of cereals reaches 4 to 5 kg/day at 300 to 400 kg live weight then roughage digestion is so much reduced that it may be preferable to use complete cereal diets and feed the roughage to other stock. As mentioned several times, the extent of cereal processing must be as little as possible, i.e. very light rolling, crimping or possibly caustic soda treatment followed by soaking before feeding.

FIGURE 30   **Overwintering of cattle on straw diets. Unlike sheep, cattle do not select the best parts of the straw but eat everything.** *Photo: Rowett Research Institute.*

Suckler cows

This form of production of calves has the advantage that it is a low-cost system as far as feed is concerned and requires a relatively low input of labour. The disadvantage, of course, is the high capital cost of the cow relative to the annual output of a weaned calf.

The nutrition of the suckler cow is almost entirely roughage based. The diet can comprise to a large extent crop by-products during the winter or dry season and grazing of arable or permanent pasture during the summer. Depending on the quality of the roughage and on the time of calving, supplements may have to be used. If the cow calves during the winter, a high protein supplement of the kind that is not destroyed in the rumen (fish meal, meat and bone meal or blood meal) should at least form part of the supplement. If untreated straw is the only roughage then it would have to be supplemented also with a small amount of an energy-rich supplement such as sugar beet pulp or cereals (Fig. 30).

CHAPTER 10

DAIRY COW NUTRITION

Of the many feeding systems for ruminants, the dairy cow is without doubt the animal that has received the greatest attention. There are a number of reasons for this. The dairy cow has been the backbone of livestock production in most European countries. It has provided the milk for liquid consumption, cheese and many other delicacies. By-products such as skimmed milk and whey in turn have helped to sustain pig production.

The dairy cow normally achieves a much greater output of protein and fat than the growing animal. She will also eat more and because of the increase in the costs of operating modern dairy units there has been a considerable incentive to achieve the greatest possible output per unit of feed or per cow. Here it should perhaps also be pointed out that there is, generally, a tendency to attach more prestige to milk output per cow than to net profit per cow.

Nutrition at calving

The requirements of the dairy cow towards the end of pregnancy increase due to the fast growth rate of the unborn calf. But when dairy cows start lactating, requirements increase several-fold. In fact the dairy cow has been selected, in a way, to feed several calves with milk but generally speaking she gives birth only to one. The change in output from pre-calving to lactation can well be compared to a sudden change from second gear to overdrive in a vehicle.

It is no surprise therefore that feeding and management during the first 2 to 3 months after calving set the pattern for the remainder of lactation. Early lactation is the period where the greatest skill is required on the part of the stockman.

It is worth remembering also that in recent years the average peak yield of Friesian cows has increased rapidly from about 25 kg/d to 35 to 40 kg/d. This increase has, in fact, meant that management systems that were adequate when 25 kg of milk was accepted as the peak of milk yield are no longer adequate and can indeed lead to problems if changes are not implemented to take account of higher yields.

Lead feeding

The generally accepted system of lead feeding followed by a set amount of concentrate per unit of milk is one which needs to be revised for higher yielding cows.

The greatest problem here is that the dry matter appetite of the newly calved cow is lower immediately after calving, and in order to attain a high yield large amounts of concentrate are fed. Thus concentrates, particularly cereal based concentrate, soon exceed 50 to 60% of the diet. This is aggravated by the fact that the cow will reduce her intake of roughage as more concentrate is fed. The cellulose part of the roughage will be fermented very poorly and before we know it the cow may effectively be digesting almost 100% concentrate. The cow is on a knife-edge for acidosis which if it occurs will stop her eating. This will be followed by ketosis and the cow is in trouble from which she may not completely recover, as far as milk yield is concerned. Very high concentrate feeding has other disastrous effects, and laminitis is another symptom of overfeeding with concentrate.

The system of estimating roughage consumption to supply feed for maintenance plus a yield of 5 to 10 kg of milk and 1 kg concentrate per 2.5 kg milk was adequate when peak yields were 20 to 25 kg milk. For instance, if the roughage intake was calculated to be sufficient up to a yield of 10 kg milk the concentrate consumption would be in the region of 4 to 6 kg/d. Relative to roughage intake the proportion of concentrate would vary from 30 to 40% of the total diet, and slightly less expressed relative to dry matter. This level of concentrates would generally not interfere with digestion of roughage. However, if the yield was 35 to 40 kg milk the concentrate allowance would amount to 10 to 12 kg/day. Roughage intake and roughage digestion would then be depressed as the proportion of concentrates in the diet would be 60 to 70%.

Sometimes milk quality suffers due to the reduced proportion and digestion of roughage though milk quality may be maintained by incorporating the concentrate in a complete mixed diet.

Complete diet feeding

This system, which has gained some popularity on large farms, is based on *ad libitum* feeding of the whole diet mixed together in a mechanical mixer wagon. The system ensures that the cows cannot select for or against concentrates. It is thus a system in which the herdsman or farmer decides on the composition of the whole diet but the animal decides how much of it to eat. This system achieves stability in the rumen and generally good health among the cows but, depending on the proportion of concentrate, it does not always ensure good milk quality nor does it ensure good digestion of roughage. This is because stable conditions in the rumen may well occur at a greater acidity than that tolerated by the bacteria which ferment cellulose. The result of complete diet feeding can therefore be overfat cows.

FIGURE 31 Large amounts of concentrate eaten during milking put the cow at risk of digestive problems

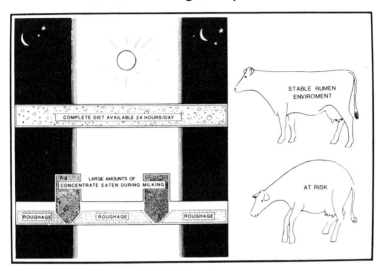

The mistake generally made by herdsmen using this system is feeding too little roughage and too much of the wrong kind of concentrate. Complete diet feeding is an excellent concept, but to be adequately exploited the maximum amount of roughage should be used to provide at least 50% of the total diet.

A number of decisions have to be made by the herdsman; the main decision is whether or not the diet is correct. Increasing the proportion of concentrate may be uneconomic or undesirable nutritionally, whilst the addition of more roughage to the diet will reduce the overall intake of ME. In most herds given complete diets there are 2 to 4 groups of cows receiving different qualities of diet. The question then is what should be the criteria of moving cows from one group to another? While the stockman has to use his judgement there are some criteria which are more suitable than others, though in some instances the optimum from a nutritional point of view has to be weighed against that which is most practicable.

Stage of lactation can be a very useful guide. For instance, cows can be kept for say 3 months in the top group. Heifers can be kept a bit longer. This approach has the advantage that if the cows are calving in batches then management is easier. If all the cows calve during a month or so it is possible only to use one diet for the whole herd.

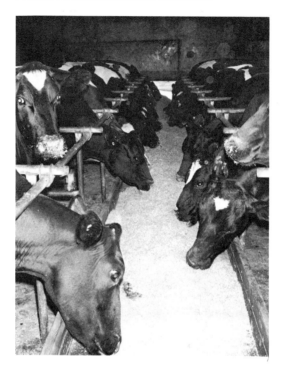

Another more difficult method is level of milk yield, with all cows above 20 kg milk in one group, and so on. In general this is not very practicable.

Regardless of the type of feed, the cow is likely to lose weight in early lactation, as discussed earlier. This should not be discouraged. However, when the cow starts increasing in weight steadily then this can only be due to the fact that she is eating more than she requires for milk production. Complete diet feeding should be combined with weekly, or even more frequent, weighing since this is the only measure that can tell whether or not the cow is eating enough or consuming too much feed. Decisions to change the diet should not be made after one weighing but on the trend in weight change. A cow yielding 20 kg of milk may well be yielding to capacity if there is no change in weight. Such cows will undoubtedly reduce milk yield when changed to a poorer diet. On the other hand, a cow yielding 35 kg milk may well consume so much feed that it is also increasing in weight and could tolerate a change to a poorer diet.

A certain amount of increase in weight may be desired before a change in diet is made. For the commercial farmer using complete diets live weight change is a very useful aid to cow management.

Flat rate feeding

Flat rate feeding means that the same quantity of concentrate is given to all cows during early and mid-lactation. The herdsman determines the level of concentrate feeding and since the cows should be offered roughage *ad libitum* they, so to speak, determine the final composition of the diet. Since roughage consumption is greatest 2 to 3 months after calving the ratio of concentrate is greatest in early lactation. This system also relies on fat mobilization as the cows are not fed to yield and are usually underfed in early lactation and overfed later.

The system can give problems of acidosis in early lactation but is simple and certainly more sound than feeding concentrate to yield in early lactation. As mentioned earlier, if body fat is to be effectively utilized the diet must contain protein to utilize the fat effectively. This means that the advantage of flat rate feeding is not so great as anticipated as the composition of the concentrate used should vary according to stage of lactation – a need which is not generally recognized.

Out of parlour feeders

Mechanical distributors are now available to enable a cow to enter a feeding bay and receive a small amount of concentrates. The number of feeds per day and the amount dispensed each time can be adjusted.

This system has some advantages, particularly if the concentrates are only given in early lactation to cows in negative energy balance. It also has the flexibility that the out-of-parlour concentrates may be high in undegraded dietary protein, for instance. The system does go some way towards achieving more stable conditions in the rumen. It does not solve all the problems and can give the same symptoms as complete diet feeding, namely overfat cows and poor milk quality, which can only be rectified by feeding a high quality roughage. However, the approach is certainly preferable to twice-daily feeding of concentrates.

Type of concentrate

The words 'concentrate' and 'cake' have different meanings to different farmers and advisers. For some they mean compound feeds, for others they mean the total amount of cereals and compound feeds. Even these definitions are inadequate. It would be more useful to define the proportion of the feed which consists of fibre and the proportion which consists of soluble sugars included in fibre, roots, or in cereals and compounds. The problem is that many by-products which are, in effect, digestible fibre are termed concentrates and are included in compounds. Conversely, the soluble sugars in hay are included in the roughage fraction.

The important point as far as the dairy cow is concerned is that digestible fibre such as that in sugar beet pulp or other crop by-products is extremely good as it ferments relatively slowly.

It is probably most important of all to pay more attention in dairy cow feeding to a move away from cereal feeding towards highly digestible by-products. If cereals are to be included in large quantities more attention has to be given to appropriate methods of cereal processing to avoid too rapid digestion.

Inclusion of fat in diets for dairy cows is sometimes advocated as a means of achieving higher intakes of energy. There are several problems here which must be remembered when fat is used. For example, too much fat can inhibit cellulose bacteria with the net result that the cows will eat less roughage. This can be avoided if the fat is used in a so-called protected form so that bacteria do not digest it in the rumen. Even so the maximum inclusion rate should not exceed 5 to 10% of dry matter and then only if the ME from fat is cheaper than ME from such items as sugar beet pulp.

Secondly, fat does not produce microbial protein. As a result the protein level in the diet must be increased accordingly. For the protein to be effective it must be the type that microbes do not degrade in the rumen. This may make the feeding of fat less attractive economically than it is sometimes made out to be.

The ability of lush summer grass to sustain high yields of milk with no further supplements is well known, but with the yields that we now wish to have even grass needs to be supplemented. If there is plenty of lush grass available the first limiting nutrient is, however, likely to be UDP. The protein in young grass is destroyed very quickly by the rumen bacteria, so although young grass is high in protein it may not contribute very much to the animal's requirement. Certainly if the cow is losing weight rapidly in early lactation on young grass it may well be that protein, more than energy, is the limiting factor. The most appropriate energy supplement for grass may well be ammonia-treated straw or sugar beet pulp, rather than cereals and roots. The soluble material in grass is already high so, in effect, it is already a mixture of fibre and concentrate.

A mixture of sugar beet pulp and protected protein or animal protein such as fishmeal, meat and bone meal or blood meal is an excellent supplement to grass, perhaps together with free access to ammonia-treated or caustic soda-treated straw.

The structure of young grass is often such that cows prefer to consume considerable quantities of fibrous roughage. Chemically-treated straw given to cows grazing early spring pasture would not depress intake of grass and would also help to ensure that the cows are healthy and that milk fat remains high.

INDEX

NOTES

NOTES